*jewelry*television®

GUIDE TO GEMS & JEWELRY

GERALD D. SISK, JR.

Jewelry Television Co-Founder

Guide to Gems & Jewelry

© 2011 America's Collectibles Network, Inc.

dba Jewelry Television®

Published by Jewelry Television®

Printed in Canada at Friesens

ISBN: 978-0-615-56239-1

For more information and the latest updates on the colorful world of gemstones, please visit **www.jtv.com.**

United States of America
Jewelry Television®
9600 Parkside Drive
Knoxville, TN 37922
United States of America

Tel: 865-692-6000
www.jtv.com

Thailand
BBJ Bangkok Ltd.
919/544, 919/605-606 Jewelry Trade Center Building, 50th Floor
Silom Road
Khwaeng Silom, Khet Bangrak, Bangkok 10500
Thailand

Tel: 02 630-3401-4

INTRODUCTION TO *GUIDE TO GEMS & JEWELRY*
TABLE OF CONTENTS

GEMSTONES FROM A–Z
TABLE OF CONTENTS

FOREWORD

Jewelry Television® is pleased to offer *Guide to Gems & Jewelry*, an authoritative and valuable resource designed exclusively for our customers, the loyal people who have made JTV successful as the largest retailer of loose gemstones in the world. Every day, we take our leadership responsibility seriously, thinking about how we can continue to bring you the knowledge and information about jewelry and gemstones that you want. So, here it is—an informative book designed just for you!

Over the years, we have learned a lot about you. Many of you are collectors of gemstones and specimens with fabulous, unique, and valuable collections. We search the world over to bring you rare, exotic gems and unique collectibles. Many of you enjoy the art of jewelry making and are constantly seeking value-priced components to include in your next design. You want fresh, timely education and creative ideas. Others of you are fashion conscious or simply enjoy the pure and timeless pleasure of classic fine jewelry.

Whatever your interest (and whether you are a "pro" or just getting started in the world of fine jewelry and gems), Jewelry Television has many products to offer. Strong relationships with international vendors enable us to introduce literally thousands of items through television and the internet. JTV stands uniquely proud that we are not merely merchants, but also educators in one of the most exciting fields of study for both the novice and the enthusiastic collector.

Mankind's love of gemstones began thousands of years ago. For example, Aaron's breastplate, a tunic adorned with 12 gems to represent the 12 tribes of Israel, is referenced in Exodus 28. (Scholars tell us that the 12 stones included emerald, turquoise, sapphire, moonstone, jasper, and carnelian.) Throughout history, gemstones have been valued for their beauty and statement of wealth. Kings and queens coveted the best of the best for crowns and scepters as well as ornamentation for thrones, palaces, and regal garments. Only in recent years have technology, distribution, and, yes, television made gemstones available in quantities large enough for us to bring to our many viewers.

This, in fact, is our mission: to make fine jewelry and gemstones available to everyone! Each year, our buyers log millions of miles, traveling around the world in pursuit of quality pearls, opals, emeralds, rubies, tanzanites, tourmalines, and more—always searching for the very best prices. Finding valuable gemstones is our core expertise, and we're energized by our quest to find the greatest value for you.

Jerry Sisk, a JTV co-founder who has led this quest for our customers, has authored this book for you. He is a scholar with a talent for explaining the captivating beauty of gemstones.

Jerry is a scientist, historian, language expert, and world traveler who understands the phenomena of gemstones, how they are formed over millions of years, where to find them, and how to bring them to life in a finished product with amazing cuts and polishes. I am honored that Jerry asked me to write the foreword for his book. It is hard to imagine anyone more dedicated to accuracy in gemstone education or with more field experience in globetrotting to some of the most remote locations in the world. Jerry began his journey as a teenager working in a New Jersey jewelry store, and he has since used his love of science and language to share what he has learned.

Jerry does not include pricing information or expectations of value relating to quality or availability. World economic conditions and supplies of gemstones fluctuate, so pricing information becomes quickly outdated. We also recognize that carat weight, cut, and quality inherently affect the value and selling price of individual gemstones. If you are a serious collector interested in tracking gem prices, we can recommend other resources to you.

Jewelry Television stands alone in the international gem trade with our buying power and staff of gemologists, buyers, and specialists. We know how fun and rewarding collecting gemstones can be, and we know that you will find Jerry's book informative and useful as you continue to enjoy the exciting world of fine jewelry and gemstones!

Tim Matthews

President and CEO
Jewelry Television®

Dreams do come true, but they usually take planning and a lot of hard work. That's how I feel about Jerry Sisk's *Guide to Gems & Jewelry.* Twenty-two years ago, while we were working at a fledgling home shopping venue, he and I first began talking about writing a book about gems and jewelry for our customers. Then in 1993, when we went out on our own and created America's Collectibles Network® (which would, of course, become Jewelry Television®), the book was always on our "dream" list. Now, the book has become a reality, and the great people of Jewelry Television are responsible for making our dream come true. Our dedicated employees and loyal customers have made JTV® the largest retailer of loose gemstones in the world, and we will always be grateful.

Bob Hall

Co-Founder and Chairman
Jewelry Television®

PREFACE

Gaius Plinius Secundus, better known as Pliny the Elder (AD 23-79), was a Roman of exceptional intellect and talent. His greatest work, *Naturalis Historia*, consisted of 37 books on a wide range of topics, including precious gemstones.

One of Pliny's often-quoted passages includes a description of a gem that has a fire softer than ruby, yet displays the brilliant purple of amethyst and the sea-green of emerald. He goes on to state that the splendor and beauty of this gem rivals all the colors of a painter's palette. Could this have been the description of a precious opal or some other exotic gem?

It is impossible to know when our ancestors first noticed a shiny, sparkling jewel in the light of day or the flame of an evening campfire. That momentous discovery could have taken place inauspiciously in the shallows of a river delta with a colorful pebble—one that was polished by a millennium of tumbling as it was inexorably pushed toward the sea. Or it might have been a crystal that shimmered in the torch light while exploring the mysteries of a dark and foreboding cave. Although that moment is lost in time, we do know that gemstones have played an integral role in myriad cultures throughout history.

While I cannot speak for our ancestors, I can tell you when and where my love of gems began. That moment occurred in the latter part of the 1950s while visiting friends in New York. Their home was a short distance from the ocean, and I remember walking along the shoreline at low tide and stopping when I saw a brightly colored pebble. Wind, water, and gravity had done their work well—my gem was smooth and rounded to the touch.

That initial discovery spurred me to search for more colorful pebbles, which I did with much gusto. Unfortunately, my parents did not share the same degree of enthusiasm for the 20-plus pounds of treasure that became my first gem collection.

As years passed and high school approached, I had the opportunity to work for a jeweler in Keyport, New Jersey. It was there that I first examined fine gemstones. That opportunity was limited, but diamonds, sapphires, emeralds, and rubies were a great starting point. (There were a few other birthstones, but the overall selection was not extensive. That was the nature of jewelry stores in the 1960s.)

As college approached, my travels took me to Knoxville, Tennessee, where I had the opportunity to work for a retail store that sold exceptionally fine jewelry. The selection was similar, but I was able to see a few more gems. This was where I encountered my first green tourmaline. It is hard to describe my excitement.

As time went by, I had the great fortune of being involved in the seminal stages of a new and growing industry—television home shopping. It provided me with the opportunity to travel to many trade shows and expand my knowledge of gemstones. My love of gems grew with every day that passed. It seemed as if there was always something new and exotic around the corner. Nature's treasures became an indelible part of my life.

Here at Jewelry Television®, we pride ourselves in providing a wide selection of exotic gems from some of the most inaccessible points on earth. Our passion for these natural treasures is evident in the variety and array of colors, shapes, sizes, and cuts we offer.

As part of this commitment, we realize that education and knowledge are important to our viewers. That is why we have taken the time to provide a handy reference guide that combines history and lore with basic gemological information. It is a great starting point for individuals who want to acquire a general knowledge of gems. We hope you find this new publication enjoyable and informative.

Jerry Sisk, G.G.
Co-Founder
Jewelry Television®

Many thanks to members of my JTV family for contributing their time and talents to this book. Pam Rader-Rousseau, Patty Reynolds, Russ Hamilton, Julie Payne, Ron Cornwell, Christopher Clark, Keith Harris, Judy Jenkins, Jami James, Donna Burns, and Joni Loveday— it's alwaysa pleasure working with you. Also, a special acknowledgement goes to Jim Wells, Barbara Boeing, and Linda Marion for production management, layout, and editorial assistance.

UNDERSTANDING GEMS

UNDERSTANDING GEMS

The beauty, rarity, and historical mystique of gems are timeless. In addition to their amazing kaleidoscopic array of colors, they also provide an exotic range of special optical properties that borders on mesmerizing. However, before you make a purchase, it will be helpful to have a basic understanding of gemstones.

What is a gem?

Ask different people this question and you will get different answers. From the perspective of a gemologist, a gemstone is a naturally occurring organic or inorganic material that possesses a certain degree of beauty, rarity, and durability. However, these three factors are relative and subjective to some extent. What one culture considers beautiful may be perceived differently by another. Some gems may be durable enough to survive the process of jewelry setting, but often require special care during wear to prolong their beauty.

In the broadest sense, some would say that a gemstone can be any material, natural or man-made, that can be used for personal adornment. In the case of man-made materials, rarity is not a factor. It should be noted, though, that some man-made gems are much more expensive to produce than others. Some types are also much more difficult to acquire.

Inorganic gemstones consist of minerals, mineraloids, and rocks. These are created by geologic processes within the earth. Organic gemstones are the product of living organisms, past or present. Pearls, coral, amber, and ivory are good examples of the latter.

Man-made gems may or may not have naturally occurring counterparts. If a natural counterpart does exist, the gem is said to be *synthetic*. Synthetic ruby and sapphire are two good examples. If a man-made gem material has no natural counterpart, it falls into the category of artificial. YAG (yttrium aluminum garnet) and GGG (gadolinium gallium garnet) are examples.

Evaluating gems

You may be familiar with the 4 C's related to the evaluation of diamond grading: color, clarity, cut, and carat weight. While professionals and connoisseurs the world over rely on these factors, it is important to understand how they are applied to gemstones.

Color: the First C

Understandably, color is the single most important factor when evaluating colored gems. Generally, the more attractive a gem's color, the higher the value. Bright, rich, and intense colors are generally coveted more than those that are too dark or too light. However, there are exceptions, such as the lovely padparadscha sapphire, which is valued for its delicate pastel hues. Color is typically defined and modified by three factors: hue, saturation, and tone. These factors are often

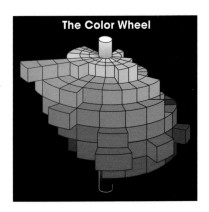

The Color Wheel

The three dimensions of color: hues change as one goes around the wheel; tone changes in the vertical axis, with the lightest tones at the top; and saturation increases from the center out on the horizontal axis.

represented in three dimensions on a color wheel to better visualize the relationships.

Hue In scientific terms, each hue is defined by a specific wavelength of light ranging from red to violet. This is the same range that you see during the formation of a rainbow. In grammar school, you may have learned this sequence by the name "Roy G Biv," a simple mnemonic device representing red, orange, yellow, green, blue, indigo, and violet.

As part of the color wheel, hue is a circular attribute. Visualize a rainbow stretched to a full 360°, with one end touching the other. One additional color, purple, is represented as an intermediate hue between red and violet. White and black are totally lacking in hue and are considered achromatic (without color). Brown is not a hue in itself, but covers a range of hues of low saturation (and often high tone). Classic browns fall in the yellow-to-orange hues.

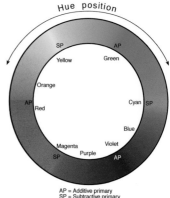

Hue position

AP = Additive primary
SP = Subtractive primary

These three green gems show a variation in hue position. The center stone is a straight green, while the stone at left is a more bluish green, and the stone at right is a slightly yellowish green. Generally speaking, hue position is of less importance than saturation in judging quality.

Generally speaking, gems that are bright red, green, and blue are most popular. This is probably due, in part, to how our eyes perceive color. Specialized cells in the retina, known as *cones,* are very sensitive to wavelengths of light that correspond to these three hues; thus, the gemstone trinity—ruby, emerald, and sapphire (aka the Big 3). However, there is much about hue that is personal and cultural, so preferences do vary.

Saturation This attribute refers to the intensity or richness of a color. It is the degree to which color varies independently of tone. When dealing with gems of the same basic hue position (i.e., rubies, which are all basically red), differences in color quality are mainly related to differences in saturation. The strong red fluorescence of most rubies is an added boost to saturation, supercharging it past other gems that lack the effect.

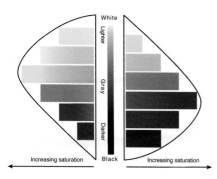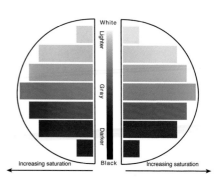

The relationship between tone (vertical axis) and saturation (horizontal axis)

2

Tone This is the degree of lightness or darkness of a color, as a function of the amount of light absorbed. White would have 0% tone, and black would be 100%. At their maximum saturations, some colors are naturally darker than others. For example, a rich violet is darker than even the most highly saturated yellow, while the highest saturations of red and green tend to be of similar tone. Note that as saturation increases, so, too, does tone (since more light is being absorbed). However, there reaches a point where increases in tone may result in a decrease in saturation as a color blackens.

When judging the quality of a gem with color, tone is an important consideration. Before buying, it's always a good idea to consider the lighting conditions under which it will be worn. Look for stones that even appear good under the low lighting conditions you find in the evening or in a restaurant, for these are typically the conditions under which fine gems are worn and viewed. Also view gems at arm's length and look for those that are attractive even at a distance. Exceptional gems tend to look great under all lighting conditions and viewing distances.

Peridot: Idiochromatic
(self-colored)

Additional notes

Minerals and their gemstone counterparts are divided into two categories when it comes to color: *idiochromatic* (self-colored) and *allochromatic* (other colored). Think of the former as *inherent* color since it is created by elements that are an integral part of the gem's chemical formula. Peridot and rhodonite are examples of idiochromatic gemstones. If the color of a gem is due to the presence of impurities (trace amounts of various transition elements), structural irregularities in the crystal lattice, or possibly a combination of the two, it is termed allochromatic.

Because tourmaline is colored by trace elements, it is an allochromatic gemstone.

The mixing of hues, such as violet-blue in tanzanite, bright blue-green in apatite, or red and orange in sapphire, can create attractive and value-enhancing combinations. Some gems also have specific expressions to denote the very top colors found within a species (e.g., cornflower blue sapphire). Such terms relate to the most desirable colors to be found within a gem species.

Although certain colors are more popular than others, personal and cultural preferences often come into play. Regardless of preference, the colors seen should ideally remain attractive regardless of prevailing light conditions. Whether viewed indoors, outdoors, by day or by night, a gem should always remain beautiful.

Clarity: the Second C

Often adding character and individuality, most gems contain tiny, natural features called *inclusions*. Many features are microscopic in nature and are best viewed under magnification, but some are larger and visible to the eye. Inclusions are a fascinating hallmark of authenticity that record a

Inclusions such as these rutile needles in ruby are often strikingly beautiful. Gemologists study inclusions for clues about the origin and nature of gems.

gem's natural relationship with the earth, and often provide insights into the origin and formation of the host. Many inclusions are highly desired by collectors (garnet crystal in diamond, horsetail inclusion in demantoid, gilalite in quartz, for example).

In general, clarity is judged by reference to the visibility of inclusions and their impact on durability. As a rule, gems with higher clarity have greater value, but there are exceptions. Magnification is often used to locate inclusions, but those that do not interfere with the brilliance and sparkle of a gem normally don't affect the value—unless durability becomes an issue. In this way, colored gems are quite different from diamond. Indeed, in certain cases, such as with Kashmir sapphires and demantoid garnets, the inclusions actually enhance beauty and value.

Clarity is important as it relates to transparency. In transparent gems, the degree of diaphaneity and light return (brilliance) is considered crucial. However, through market experience, we learn to expect certain degrees of clarity from various gemstones. Aquamarine, for example, is generally expected to be clean with no eye-visible inclusions, but its close relative, emerald, is held to a lower standard since it regularly occurs in nature with lower clarity levels.

Cut: the Third C

The function of the cut is to display the gem's inherent beauty to the greatest extent possible. Since this involves aesthetic preferences upon which there is little agreement (such as shape and faceting styles), this is the most subjective of all aspects of quality analysis.

In well-cut gems, most light returns as brilliance (left). If a gem is cut too shallow, light will pass straight through, rather than returning to the eye as brilliance. This is termed a *window* (right).

Unlike diamonds, gemstones possess variable optical properties, and thus are not often cut to a uniform standard. A well-cut gemstone exhibits even color, an acceptable number of inclusions for the type, and good brilliance. One of the primary considerations for a lapidary (gem cutter) is the balance between carat weight retention and beauty.

In addition to variable optical properties, gemstones commonly vary in specific gravity (relative density). Two one-carat round brilliant-cut diamonds will each be about 6.5mm in diameter. However, the same cannot be said of two one-carat gemstones of different species. If you were to compare the diameter of a round one-carat zircon to that of fire opal, you would notice a significant difference in diameter—sometimes greater than 2mm. Zircon is much denser than opal and packs more mass into the same volume of space. To compensate for differences in specific gravity, the gemstone industry came up with calibrations. A calibrated gemstone has industry-accepted dimensions for length and width. Jewelry manufacturers design many pieces to accommodate these standard shapes and sizes.

Broadly speaking, the fashioning of gems can be divided into two basic groups: faceted and non-faceted. The choice of style is often determined by the degree of clarity or the presence of special optical properties.

Faceted gemstones have geometrically shaped flat or concave surfaces and normally consist of a crown (top portion), pavilion (bottom portion), and girdle (a thin band that separates the crown from the pavilion). The girdle may be rough, polished, or even faceted.

Non-faceted gems lack angled, geometric surfaces. Most gems without facets are cut *en cabochon*. This style of fashioning, commonly referred to as a *cab*, primarily consists of a flat bottom and a polished dome of varying height. In some cases, the bottom may also be domed, creating a double cab.

Phenomenal gems exhibiting special optical properties such as asterism (stars) and chatoyancy (cat's eyes) must be fashioned en cabochon. Without the domed surface of the cab, their effects would be lost. Star sapphire and cat's-eye chrysoberyl are two well-known examples of gems cut en cabochon.

In some cases, a blended style of cut may be seen. Gems known as *buff tops*, for example, have faceted pavilions and polished, domed crowns.

It is important to note that cut and shape are two different attributes. Shape refers to the outline or form of a gemstone. Round, oval, square, heart, and cushion are examples of shapes. Almost any style of cutting can be applied to these. An oval gem, for example, may have a step cut, mixed step cut, flower cut, modified brilliant cut, or even a concave cut. Many other possibilities exist.

The beauty and liveliness of a gem are dependent on many factors. Optical properties play an important role, but so do symmetry, proportions, and finish. The size, shape, number, angle, and placement of facets have a significant impact on visual appeal. Faceted gems should not be lopsided or irregular in form. Generally, if divided down the middle, each half should be a mirror image of the other. Finish, which encompasses factors such as misshapen facets, poor polish, and rounded facet edges, also plays an important role.

Two negatives associated with faceted gems are *windows* and *extinction*. Windows occur when gems are cut too shallow, allowing a substantial amount of light to pass through, rather than returning to the eye in the form of brilliance. It is actually possible to read text through a gemstone suffering from this condition. The other extreme is extinction, which occurs on deeper cuts. Extinction manifests as darker, lifeless areas within a gem. It is most noticeable in larger, more heavily saturated stones.

In essence, it is important that a cut display a gem's beauty to its best advantage, while not creating issues with setting or durability. If a gem is visually appealing, details such as the depth percentage or length-to-width ratio matter not a bit. What works, works. The eye, the mind, and the heart are the final arbiters, not the numbers.

One final note about cut: the most expensive gemstones (particularly colored diamonds and rubies) are often not cut to ideal proportions and symmetry. This is because the value of the material is so high that the cutter strives to save every point in weight.

Carat weight: the Fourth C

Gemstone weight is measured in *carats*. These archaic units of measurement originate from the traditional use of carob seeds to weigh gems in the bazaars of the Middle East and Asia. Carob seeds were used because of their consistent size and shape, but unity of weight was still an issue from country to country and city to city. The carat was ultimately tied to the metric system and standardized as one fifth of a gram (one carat equals .20 grams or, conversely, 5 carats equal one gram).

A carat was further divided into 100 smaller units called *points*. A 50-point gemstone, for example, would be the same as a half-carat, and a 25-point stone equivalent to one-quarter carat. Europe converted to the metric carat in 1907. The USA followed suit in 1913.

One three-carat gemstone is usually worth more than three one-carat gemstones.

The term *carat* (abbreviated ct) is often confused with *karat* (abbreviated Kt or K). Karat is a measure of gold purity (fineness) and has no relationship to carat, which is a metric unit of mass.

Generally, as the weight of a gem increases, so does its price per carat. Large gems are rarer than smaller ones, so per-carat prices can rise exceptionally. For example, a 3ct ruby is always worth far more than three 1ct rubies of the same quality.

The only time smaller gems may cost more than a single gem of the same carat weight is when labor becomes a factor. Applying facets to 50 two-point amethysts, for example, would make the 50 smaller stones more expensive than a single 1ct gem of the same quality.

Gemstone prices also increase rapidly when in excess of certain key weights. For example, a 2.01ct ruby has a higher price tag than a 1.99ct ruby, despite a negligible difference in actual size. Gem pricing is therefore based on a *nonlinear scale of increments*. To put this into context, a 16ct ruby sold at Sotheby's in New York in October 1988 for a staggering $3,630,000. If gem pricing was linear, that would make a similar 1ct ruby worth $226,875.

Color coverage: the Fifth C

When evaluating gems, we are not dealing with opaque, matte-finish objects of uniform color. Thus, it is not enough to simply describe hue position, saturation, and tone. While the first "Four C's" are commonly encountered in many marketing brochures and websites, the "Fifth C" is not as well known. It is, however, an important factor.

Color coverage considers the uniformity or distribution of color and takes into account the visual impact of scintillation and dispersion. It can be modified by the style of cutting, proportions, transparency, inclusions, fluorescence, pleochroism, and zoning. Generally, a gem with a higher degree of color coverage is more valuable.

Proper cutting is vital to maximize color coverage. If a gemstone is cut with a large bulge on the pavilion, it creates uneven distribution of color. If looking at the stone through the table (largest facet on the crown), the central portion will appear lighter, and the perimeter will appear darker or even black.

The effects of pleochroism in green tourmaline: along the vertical axis, a bluish green color is seen, while along the horizontal axis, the color is yellowish green. This is a product of the doubly refractive nature of tourmaline.

Gems cut too shallow permit only short light paths, thus reducing saturation. Such areas often appear lighter and windowed. The opposite occurs when gems are cut too deeply. This creates an area that appears dark and lifeless, which is described as *extinction*. An important goal of cutting is to maximize internal reflection, which will improve the liveliness of the gem as well as the saturation of colors. Internal reflection of light is described in terms of *brilliance*.

Color zoning can also reduce color coverage. It is common in some allochromatic gems, such as sapphire. Color zoning often appears as a series of lighter or darker areas within the host. The zoning may appear as lines, bands, or even amorphous areas that contrast with the overall color of the gem. It is due to changing conditions during the formation of a crystal.

Moderate color zoning in tourmaline

Ideally, no zoning should be present in a gem. Moderate-to-severe color zoning does impact quality and, thus, price. Color zoning is always judged in the face-up position, in a 180° arc from girdle to girdle with the gem rotated through 360°. Zoning visible only through the pavilion generally does not impact value.

Inclusions may have a positive or negative impact on color coverage. Tiny, light-scattering inclusions, such as rutile silk, can actually improve coverage and, thus, appearance by scattering light into areas it would not otherwise strike. The end effect is to give the gem a warm, velvety appearance (Kashmir sapphires are famous for this). Red fluorescence in ruby boosts this still further.

Pleochroism is noticeable face-up in some gems such as some tourmalines and iolite. It typically appears as two areas of lower intensity and/or slightly different hue on opposite sides of the stone.

In summary, a top-quality gem would display the hue of maximum saturation across a large percentage of its surface in all viewing positions. The closer a gem approaches this ideal, the better its color coverage.

Country of origin

Names of geographical locations should only be used when they denote the areas from which gemstones originate. For example, it is misleading to call a high-quality emerald *Colombian* if it doesn't actually come from Colombia.

While there are exceptions, gemstones that are rich in history and folklore are generally more prized than those lacking historical connotations. A ruby from Burma (Myanmar), for example, often commands a premium over rubies of similar quality from other countries.

When specifying an origin, Jewelry Television® undertakes a series of checks based on our experience to ensure that a gemstone displays the characteristics indicative of the origin specified. While Jewelry Television does everything possible to ensure that the origins we specify are correct, gemstone origin is often impossible to determine. Even experts are unable to agree on the origins of certain gems.

Durability

"The love of precious gemstones is deeply implanted in the human heart," wrote George Kunz in his book, *The Curious Lore of Precious Stones*.

"The cause of this must be sought not only in their coloring and brilliancy but also their durability," Kunz further wrote, "The sheen and coloration of precious stones are the same today as they were thousands of years ago and will be for thousands of years to come. In a world of change, this permanence has a charm of its own that was early appreciated."

A gemstone must be durable enough not to break or fade over years of wear. Its brilliance and beauty are expected to last for a very long time, even to the point where a gemstone will outlast its owners and be passed on to sons and daughters, who, in turn, will help maintain its status as a gem by awakening appreciation in succeeding generations. While gems with better durability

Diamonds may be the hardest gems, but they are not the toughest.

Jade is an example of a gemstone that is not particularly hard, but extremely tough.

and resistance to wear are generally more highly prized than those of lesser durability, given proper care, all gemstone jewelry should be suitable to be passed down to many generations.

Durability is a combination of three properties:

1. **Hardness**: This is the ability of a gem to resist surface scratching. Hardness is quantified on a comparative scale that ranges from 1 to 10, with a 10 being the hardest and 1 the softest. The system was devised in the 18th century by Viennese mineralogist Friederich Mohs and is named after him (Mohs' hardness scale). The minerals chosen for the scale set the level of hardness.

2. **Toughness**: This is the ability of a gem to resist chipping and breakage. Damage may occur from fracture (random non-directional breaks) or cleavage (splitting along planes of growth within a crystal).

Scratch Hardness (Mohs)	Comparative minerals
1	Talc
2	Gypsum
3	Calcite
4	Fluorite
5	Apatite
6	Orthoclase
7	Quartz
8	Topaz
9	Corundum
10	Diamond

3. **Stability**: This is the ability of a gem to remain unaltered in the presence of chemicals, heat, light, and weathering.

Rarity

By their very definition, all gems are rare. Rarity can be described in three, often unrelated, ways:

- Geological
- Marketplace
- Comparative

While scarcer gems are generally more highly prized than less scarce varieties, geological rarity doesn't always mean a gem has a higher value in the marketplace and vice versa. Beauty and marketing play a big part. Sometimes, the geological rarity of a gem type jeopardizes commercial viability. Tsavorite garnet is rarer than emerald and is sometimes more beautiful, but because of its rarity, it cannot compete with emerald in terms of the consumer perception of its value. Given the enormous diamond stockpiles and new sources springing up around the world, when compared to many colored gemstones, diamonds are not especially rare. Strict control of polished diamond supply in the market, combined with sophisticated consumer advertising, have elevated diamonds to the extent that they are perceived as a rare and coveted product.

If a gem variety is so rare that it is essentially unknown to the general public, it is often classified as an *exotic* or *collector's gem*. Gems such as boracite, childrenite, and simpsonite are extremely rare, attractive, and durable, but they are unlikely to command prices appropriate to their rarity because few people are aware of their existence.

Tanzanite pair

Pairs and suites

Pairs, or suites, of gems matched for color, clarity, and cut are valued more highly per carat or per gem than single gems of the same quality. Given the rarity of many gems, a matching set is disproportionately hard to find and will command a higher per-carat price than if each of the gems from the suite was sold separately.

Peridot suite photographed by Jeff Scovil; stones provided by Barker & Co.

LUSTER, BRILLIANCE & FIRE

LUSTER, BRILLIANCE & FIRE

These frequently used terms to describe the visual appearance of the interaction between light and a gem are often confused and misused, sometimes even by experienced industry professionals. The following clears up the confusion, allowing you to understand exactly what you are seeing when you gaze upon your gemstone jewelry.

Luster (external brilliance)

Luster is the quality and quantity of light reflected from a gem's surface and is a function of refractive index and surface perfection (degree of polish).

If nearly all the light falling upon a gem's surface is reflected, resulting in a very bright appearance, it is said to have *high luster*. If much of the light is absorbed by the gem, resulting in a dull reflection, it is said to have *low luster*. Luster is generally divided into two major categories: *metallic* and *non-metallic*.

Adjectives commonly used to describe luster include:

Luster is the surface reflection of light.

1. **Metallic:** This is a very high luster that has the appearance of polished metal. Hematite, pyrite, and cuprite are examples of minerals that may exhibit this degree of luster.
2. **Submetallic:** This is used to describe minerals having the look of polished metal dulled by weathering or wear. Nearly opaque gems that reflect well fall into this category. Sphalerite and cuprite often exhibit this type of luster.
3. **Adamantine:** This is the brightest, most reflective non-metallic luster. It is characteristic of gems with higher refractive indices (e.g., diamond and demantoid garnet).
4. **Subadamantine:** This term is used to describe gems that have a bright luster approaching that of diamond (e.g., certain varieties of zircon and garnet).
5. **Vitreous:** This luster is seen in polished glass and in most transparent gemstones whose refractive indices fall within the middle range of values (e.g., emerald and tourmaline).
6. **Resinous:** This luster is characteristic of certain gems with low-to-moderate refractive indices. It has the appearance of polished plastic. Amber exhibits resinous luster.
7. **Silky:** This type of luster is characteristic of certain gems that have an extremely fine fibrous structure. Examples include ulexite, gypsum, and malachite.
8. **Pearly:** As this adjective implies, it is descriptive of the luster seen in pearls and is used to describe any mineral or gem that has a similar appearance. Examples include muscovite, talc, and the shell of various mollusks.

A common misconception is that high luster is better. Certainly for colorless gems such as diamond, this is the case, but for gems that depend on their color for beauty, a high luster is actually an impediment since it prevents light from entering the gem. This is why the colors of high refractive index (RI) gems, such as diamonds, are often somewhat "steely," while the colors of lower RI gems, such as emeralds, can be so beautiful.

Brilliance

Brilliance refers to the amount of light returned to the eye from the interior of a gem and is mainly a function of refractive index, proportions, and transparency.

Faceted gems are designed to catch all possible light and throw it back to the eye. If the gem is cut too shallow, light from above and below passes straight through. This creates a *window,* where one can see through the gem. Thus, brilliance suffers.

Similarly, if the gem is cut too deep, light from above passes out the side. This creates areas of darkness, known as *extinction.* Again, brilliance suffers (and there's nothing worse than suffering brilliance).

A gem's potential brilliance is mainly a function of refractive index (RI), with higher RI gems having more potential brilliance. But as we learned with luster, a high RI can actually hurt the display of color. Thus, one should not worry too much about RI. The main thing is to look for stones that are of good proportions—not too shallow, nor too deep. Overly deep stones have the double disadvantage of being more difficult to set in jewelry.

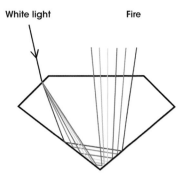

White light **Fire**

When a gem splits light into its component colors, it is said to have *fire.*

It is important to note that gem cutting is an art form rather than a formula. What works best is simply what works best—that which brings out the greatest beauty in the gem. Since judgment of beauty is by definition subjective, quality of cutting is also a matter of opinion.

Fire

Fire is a manifestation of the optical property known as *dispersion.* Dispersion occurs when light moves from one medium to another (e.g., air to gemstone). Each wavelength of light (i.e., red, orange, yellow, green, blue, and violet) slows and is bent to a different degree. The result is that light no longer appears white. The effect is often demonstrated with the aid of a prism. In general usage, both terms are often applied interchangeably.

The effects of dispersion are probably best known in diamond; however, many gemstones with higher refractive indices also exhibit significant fire. Examples include cerussite, demantoid garnet, and sphene.

Stone size and color can both affect fire. Larger gems are able to spread light to a greater degree because of the longer light paths. This helps dispersion. Color, as it becomes more intense, tends to mask the effect.

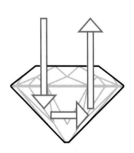

A well-cut gem should maximize the light reflected through the top of the gem.

With too shallow a cut, light passes straight through the gem.

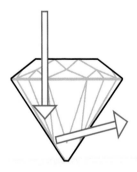

With too deep a cut, the light will not be returned to the eye. Instead, it exits the side.

GEMSTONES

GEMSTONES

The earth produces a wide range of treasures for mankind. Many of these make their way into jewelry for the purpose of adornment. Others may be carved or fashioned into utilitarian objects such as knives, arrowheads, or bowls. Art and décor also provide motivation for the creative manipulation of nature's treasures. Gemstones come from many sources.

Gemstones

Most gemstones start life as minerals, or to a much lesser extent, mineraloids. Additionally, some gems may be the product of living organisms, past or present. The latter are known as *organic gems* and include materials such as pearl, amber, and coral.

Gemstones, like the animal kingdom, have a hierarchy of taxonomy. They are discussed in terms of *groups, species,* and *varieties.* A group is the broadest stroke and contains a series of mineral species that have similar chemical composition and structure. Variations within each species are defined as varieties. Varieties are designated by color, special optical properties known as *phenomena,* or some combination of the two.

**Cultured Tahitian pearl
(organic gemstone)**

Generally, gemstones are divided into two groups:

Macrocrystalline: these are single-piece crystals visible to the naked eye. Most transparent gemstones fall into this category (e.g., ruby, sapphire, emerald, and tourmaline).

Microcrystalline: these are aggregates of crystals too small to be seen without the aid of standard magnification (e.g., aventurine quartz). **Cryptocrystalline** aggregates are so minute that no distinct grains are visible without the aid of extreme magnification (e.g., chalcedony quartz).

Emerald

Red spinel in calcite

Rubellite tourmaline

Minerals

Minerals are naturally occurring, solid, inorganic materials that have a well-defined crystal structure. The crystal structure is created by an orderly, repeating, three-dimensional pattern of atoms. These structures have various characteristics that allow minerals to be divided into six crystal systems (seven in older texts).

Agodi rubellite tourmaline mineral crystal

The external expression of the internal pattern of atoms is known as a *habit*. Habits can vary due to differences in the environment during the time of formation. Specimens of these habits are highly prized by collectors, a factor that often limits the availability of certain rare and exotic gems. Many mineral crystals that can potentially be cut into gemstones never make the journey to a lapidary's wheel. In many respects, this is understandable since well-formed crystal specimens are truly natural works of art. A secondary consideration is that many exotic mineral crystals have extremely low yield. It is not unusual to destroy more than 90% of a specimen to recover a few carats of gems.

Currently, more than 4,000 minerals have been identified, with more being added yearly. Many never make the transition to the realm of gemstones due to durability or beauty. Some are too soft or unstable to be cut for use in jewelry manufacture. Others do not have the rich, vibrant colors that attract the eye of consumers and designers. However, many minerals that never make it into mainstream jewelry are often cut to meet the demand of collectors who are always on the lookout for rare and exotic gems.

Mineraloids

Mineral-like substances that do not exhibit a crystal structure fall into this category. Generally, mineraloids are amorphous. Examples include obsidian, moldavite, and opal.

Rocks

The final member of the group is rock. A rock is an aggregate that consists of two or more minerals and, sometimes, organic materials. Examples include maw-sit-sit, unakite, and lapis lazuli. Many rocks are used for jewelry manufacture, but also find their way into decorative pieces and objet d'art.

OPTICAL EFFECTS

OPTICAL EFFECTS

Some gemstones exhibit special optical properties known as *phenomena* (*phenomenon* is singular) and are referred to as *phenomenal gems*. These special optical effects often increase the desirability of the host material, adding value in the process. Many popular phenomena are highly coveted by collectors and designers alike.

It is the possession of different crystal structures offered by many gemstones that gives them their unique properties. Without these unique properties, our ancestors would have never valued them as unusual, rare, desirable, or beautiful, and in turn, without them, our gemstone choices would be very limited.

Adularescence
This optical effect is typically associated with moonstone, a member of the feldspar family. It manifests as a soft shimmer or billowy light that moves within the gemstone as it is rocked back and forth. It is an interference phenomenon created by the layered structure of the gem.

Asterism
Asterism is a star-like pattern that is created when light encounters parallel, fibrous, or needle-like inclusions within a gem. Light striking the inclusions is reflected, creating a narrow band or line. When two or more intersecting bands of light appear, a star pattern is formed. Depending on the structure of the gem, there may be four, six, or less commonly, twelve rays.

Moonstone displaying its characteristic adularescence

Gems exhibiting this optical effect are referred to as *star gems* and are described as *asteriated*. Common examples include star sapphire, ruby, and spinel.

Gemstones will exhibit this effect when:

1. The inclusions are long and needle shaped

2. The inclusions are in parallel arrangements in at least two directions

3. The inclusions are sufficiently abundant

4. The gem is cut with a domed top (en cabochon)

5. The base of the domed gem is parallel to the direction in which the inclusions lie

Star ruby's asterism

The quality and value of a star gem are judged by:

1. The definition and intensity of the effect
2. The length and degree of straightness of each ray
3. The saturation and uniformity of the gem's color
4. The position of the star (how well centered for the shape)
5. The gem's size and carat weight

Proper lighting is very important when viewing star gems. The effect is much stronger under single light sources, such as penlights, fiber optic lights, or direct sunlight. Diffused illumination, which is commonly used in television studios, tends to minimize the effect.

Aventurescence

Gems exhibiting this phenomenon appear to have speckles that sparkle in the light. The glittery effect is created by the presence of plate-like or leaf-like inclusions interspersed throughout the gem. Light encountering these myriad obstructions is reflected back to the viewer.

The best-known example of this optical property occurs in aventurine quartz (after which the phenomenon is named). Another common example occurs in aventurescent oligoclase feldspar, known as *sunstone*.

Sunstone displaying its characteristic aventurescence

Labradorescence

This optical property manifests as a metallic iridescence (called *schiller*). The effect is commonly associated with spectrolite and labradorite, the latter lending its name to the phenomenon.

The iridescent play of colors occurs when light encounters layers of feldspar of variable thickness and composition. Some light is reflected back and some refracted down. This occurs many times, and, ultimately, myriad wavelengths of light recombine in a constructive or destruction manner, intensifying or lessening color, dependent on the type and degree of interference.

Labradorite

Ammolite's iridescence breaks light into its spectral colors.

Iridescence

This is a rainbow-like color effect seen in some gems. It is caused by cracks or structural layers breaking up light into spectral colors. Fire agate is a gemstone that shows this phenomenon to good effect. When iridescence occurs in metallic hues in gemstones such as labradorite and spectrolite, it is commonly called *labradorescence*. In pearls, the subtle iridescence is called *orient*.

Play of color

This special optical effect is most commonly associated with precious opal. It appears as flashes of rainbow colors that change with the angle of viewing. It is due to a combination of light diffraction and interference. In the case of opal, small silica spheres are responsible for the effect. The color seen is dependent on the size of the spheres, their uniformity, alignment, and other factors. This should not be confused with *opalescence*, which is the milky-blue or pearly appearance of opal, caused by the reflection of light.

Play of color in
Lightning Ridge black opal

Chatoyancy

This special optical property is similar in many ways to asterism; however, only one ray is present. It appears as a single bright line or band of light across the surface of a gem. The name comes from the French term *oeil de chat*, meaning *eye of cat*, an allusion to the feline characteristic it resembles.

The requirements for a cat's eye are similar to those for asterism, but if more than one line or ray exists, the effect is considered a star. This phenomenon is best seen on gems cut *en cabochon*.

Cat's-eye gems require:

1. Long, parallel, needle-shaped inclusions
2. A sufficient abundance of inclusions
3. A gem with a curved or domed top (cut en cabochon)
4. A base that lies parallel to the direction of the inclusions

Cat's-eye chrysoberyl
displaying chatoyancy

One of the most coveted cat's-eye gems is chrysoberyl—so much so, that if you just mention the term *cat's eye*, it is assumed to be in reference to cat's-eye chrysoberyl. All other cat's-eye gems must include the species or variety name (e.g., cat's-eye quartz, cat's-eye indicolite, and cat's-eye apatite).

Color change

This unique optical property is sometimes called the *alexandrite effect*, since alexandrite is the most famous of all color-change gemstones (a color-change variety of chrysoberyl). Very few gems exhibit this special property, and the few that do are highly prized by gem collectors throughout the world.

Color change occurs in the presence of white light, but not

Color-change
blue garnet

all white light is equal. Some sources are more balanced than others are. North daylight (in the northern hemisphere; south daylight in the southern hemisphere) is generally well balanced. Incandescent (tungsten) light, on the other hand, contains little in the blue end of the spectrum, and, thus, looks slightly yellow.

Certain gems transmit strongly in the blue and red portions of the spectrum, but they absorb the yellow. In daylight, such gems appear greenish since our eyes are most sensitive to green light. However, the same gem under an incandescent source is missing blue light. This tips the balance to the red side, and the gem appears reddish. Such gems are said to display a change of color.

This effect was first noticed when a special type of chrysoberyl was unearthed in Russia's emerald mines. According to the legend, the finder took it to be a fine emerald and decided to present it to the local king. In the candlelight of the palace, as the box holding the gem was opened, inside lay a small, purplish gem resembling nothing so much as a small amethyst. Taking it to be an insult, the ruler ordered the man to be executed, but as the sun rose the following day, the king again looked at the gem. He found it to be green and, thus, spared the miner's life. Oh, those capricious kings.

Apart from the standard factors used to assess gemstones, the quality and value of a color-change gem is judged by the strength of the color change. The ideals are an emerald green in daylight and a ruby red in incandescent light, but these are rarely ever found. Most color-change gems go from a bluish green in daylight to a purplish red in incandescent light. Examples of gemstones that exhibit color change include sapphire, spinel, tourmaline, garnet, and diaspore.

Double refraction & pleochroism
Gems that form in any crystal system other than isometric (cubic) possess the property of double refraction. Double refraction occurs when a single beam of light is split into two component rays, each of which travels in a different direction and, generally, at different speeds. The degree of separation of these two rays is termed *birefringence*. This optical *doubling* effect produces a twin image of facets when one looks through the gem. If the birefringence is strong enough, doubling may even be seen with the naked eye—calcite being the classic example.

Another effect related to double refraction is the property of *pleochroism*. Not only can each ray be bent a different amount, but each may be absorbed to a different degree. This means that component rays may not contain the same wavelengths of visible light, thus appearing different in color. This difference in selective absorption is responsible for pleochroism (pleo = many, chroma = color).

White zircon

Blue zircon

Pleochroism is entirely independent of birefringence and can be further defined by its crystal system. Dimetric (tetragonal, hexagonal) crystals have the potential to show two different colors. This is known as *dichroism,* and the gems are said to be *dichroic.* Trimetric (orthorhombic, monoclinic, triclinic) crystals may show up to three colors (but only two in any one direction). Gems in this group are more precisely described as *trichroic.* They exhibit the property of *trichroism.*

Both pleochroism and double refraction result from distortions of the crystal lattice. With *isometric* crystals (e.g., diamond, spinel, garnet), the structure is effectively a perfect sphere, where each direction of growth is identical to any other. Thus, light is affected the same in all directions. These crystals have only one refractive index and no pleochroism.

Now, if one were to take that sphere and stretch it a bit, suddenly, there are two distinct directions. Looking down the end, it is still perfectly round, but perpendicular to the end, it is egg shaped. These *dimetric* crystals will have two refractive indices and may show two colors (dichroism).

If, however, one were to take that egg shape and distort it further by squashing it on one side, suddenly, you have created a shape where all three dimensions are different. These *trimetric* crystals have three refractive indices and the potential to display three different colors (trichroism).

As one rotates a pleochroic gem, the eye blends the two colors together. Differences, if they exist, will be seen in different directions. A special gemological tool, known as a *dichroscope,* allows the viewer to see the individual colors when present.

When cutting strongly pleochroic gems (e.g., kunzite, tourmaline), lapidaries try to minimize the pleochroism and maximize the single best color. An exception is andalusite, where cutters try to orient the gem to get a pleasing mix of oranges, yellows, and greens.

Many gemstones are pleochroic, but the two component colors seen by the eyes are so similar that the pleochroism is not particularly visible. Examples of weak-to-medium pleochroic gems are ruby, sapphire, emerald, and chrysoberyl.

Due to their crystal structure, some gemstones do not possess pleochroism. This lack of pleochroism is an extremely useful diagnostic tool. Ruby and red spinel, for example, share many similar characteristics, and one way of distinguishing between the two is to test for pleochroism. Notable examples of non-pleochroic gems are spinel, garnet, and diamond.

Andalusite/greenish

Andalusite/reddish

GEMSTONE FORMATION

For millions of years, gemstones have formed beneath the surface of the earth in a variety of different environments.

Traditionally, the rocks in which gems form fall into three rock classifications: igneous (magmatic), metamorphic, and sedimentary. Igneous rocks crystallize from molten magma, lava, or gases. Sedimentary rocks crystallize from hydrous solutions on or near the earth's surface, while metamorphic rocks re-crystallize from existing minerals that have been subjected to great pressure and high temperatures.

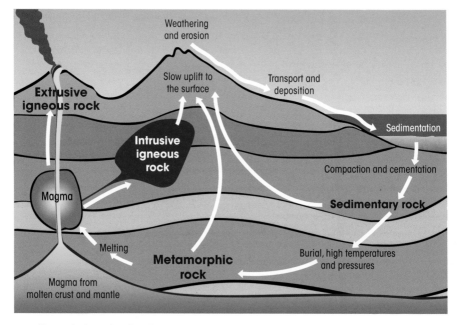

The geologic cycle: all rocks begin as igneous, but later can be transformed, via weathering, into sedimentary rocks; via heat and pressure, they can be transformed into metamorphic rocks.

Gemstone formation is generally classified into four processes:

1. Molten rock and associated fluids
2. Environmental changes
3. Surface water
4. Formation in the earth's mantle

While potentially confusing, it should be noted that some gemstone varieties are formed by more than one process.

Molten rock and associated fluids

Molten rock and associated fluids are minerals that are formed in the magma or its escaping fluids. They are created by heat deep within the earth. Molten rock and associated fluids are further classified into magma crystallization, gas crystallization, hydrothermal, and pegmatites.

Magma crystallization

As magma cools, its various elements combine to form minerals. When one mineral forms, the available ingredients, temperature, and pressure gradually change to create different minerals. While one mineral will occasionally crystallize, if the conditions are not suitable, no large crystals will form; instead, the magma will simply cool into aggregate rocks (i.e., solid masses of small, interlocking crystals).

Before all the magma can crystallize, it will break into the crust and rush toward the earth's surface. When the pressure and temperature are too low for crystallization, the rest of the magma cools into fine-grained rocks with the original crystals distributed in *phenocrysts* throughout the rocks' interiors. Gems formed in these conditions include ruby, sapphire, moonstone, garnet, and zircon.

Gas crystallization

While some gems grow on a solid base, others form inside gas bubbles. Gas bubbles are formed during a volcanic eruption when rising magma undergoes a rapid reduction in pressure. These bubbles often contain high concentrations of certain elements, and with the right combination of temperature and pressure, gems including garnet, topaz, and spinel are formed.

Hydrothermal

Hydrothermal liquids are created when water and heat interact with magma deep inside the earth. These liquids contain water, carbon dioxide, special elements (such as fluorine and beryllium), and volatiles (substances that are readily vaporized) that have escaped from the magma through fractures and fissures. Hydrothermal liquids may dissolve minerals or combine with ground water as they solidify and form mineral veins. If combined with the right temperature, pressure, time, and physical space, gems including amethyst, topaz, and emerald are formed.

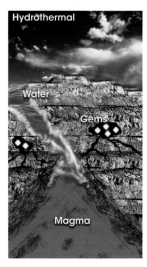

Pegmatites

When magma in the upper part of the mantle becomes concentrated with volatiles, it cools into a cavity called a *pegmatite*. As the molten rock begins to solidify, the elements begin to crystallize into gems including topaz, tourmaline, kunzite, aquamarine, and morganite.

Environmental changes

Environmental changes such as changes in temperature or pressure can alter existing minerals into something new. This process is called *metamorphism*, and it is divided into two types: contact metamorphism and regional metamorphism.

1. **Contact metamorphism** Contact metamorphism occurs when magma forces its way into an existing rock. The intense heat melts these rocks and re-crystallizes new minerals that are stable at higher temperatures. Gemstones formed by contact metamorphism include garnet, diopside, spinel, and lapis lazuli.

2. **Regional metamorphism** The earth is composed of continental plates that float on the mantle. As some of them compete for the same space, their interaction is responsible for the formation of geographic features like mountains. The intense heat and pressure generated by these geological events can cause minerals to become unstable, changing them into new varieties over time. *Polymorphs* are gemstones that re-crystallize into a new crystal system during regional metamorphism. Examples include andalusite, kyanite, sillimanite, tanzanite, and some varieties of garnet. In contrast, *pseudomorphs* like tiger's eye change their chemistry through atom-by-atom replacement during regional metamorphism.

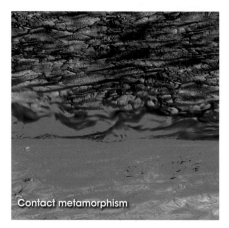

Contact metamorphism

Surface water

Rain plays an important role in recycling minerals and creating new gems. As water passes through the earth, it picks up various chemicals that can react with each other in a variety of ways. When a dry season occurs after a period of heavy rainfall, water tables fall, leaving behind deposits of different minerals in seams and cavities. Depending on what chemicals the water has reacted with, gemstones including opal, turquoise, malachite, amethyst, agate, and azurite are created.

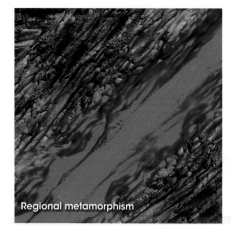

Regional metamorphism

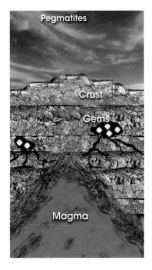

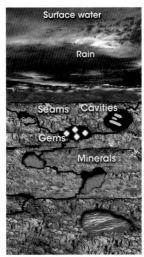

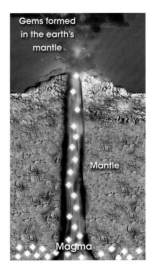

Gems formed in the earth's mantle

The earth's mantle is composed of molten rock and gases called *magma*. It is 83% of the earth's volume and 1,864 miles thick. Near the center, the mantle is extremely hot and kept in constant motion due to currents of heat. Where the mantle and crust meet, a tumultuous zone of high pressure and temperature is created.

Peridot and diamond are examples of gemstones that crystallize at extremely high temperatures. Peridot deposits in Arizona were created on rocks floating in the mantle, approximately 20–55 miles below the earth's surface. Diamonds crystallize in the magma approximately 100–150 miles below the earth's surface, where the temperatures are higher and the magma is very fluid.

MINING GEMSTONES

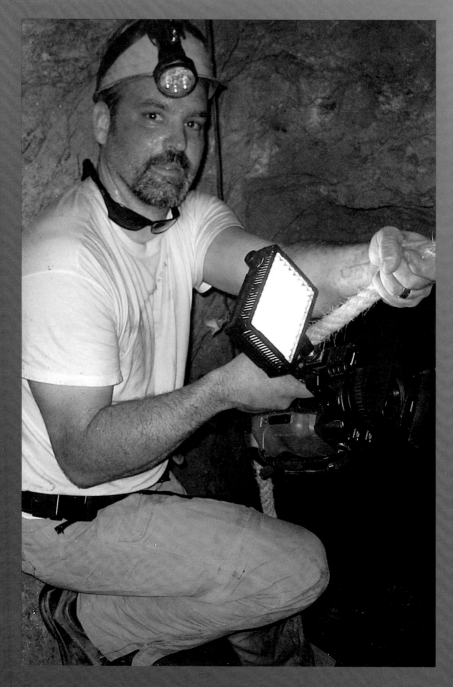

MINING GEMSTONES

In antiquity, most gemstones were discovered near the surface, generally by accident. While this has somewhat changed in modern times, prospecting for colored gemstones is still a fairly primitive affair, relying more on observation and chance than the intensive, scientific methods employed by the large, multi-national corporations involved in diamond exploration.

One of the most intriguing aspects of gemstone mining is the diversity of techniques employed in their extraction. These range from low-tech tools such as shovels and sieves to the high-tech methods used to extract diamonds from pipes (a volcanic pathway that connects the earth's deep mantle to the surface). Apart from the introduction of power tools and pumps, most colored gem mining hasn't changed dramatically in thousands of years and still relies on three key things—perseverance, hand tools, and elbow grease.

With a radiocarbon age of 43,000 years, the oldest known mine is the Lion Cave in Swaziland.

Washing alluvial gem gravels near Ilakaka, Madagascar

At this site, people mined the iron-containing mineral hematite, which they presumably ground to produce the red pigment *ochre*. Sites of a similar age were also found by archaeologists in the Netherlands and Hungary, which may have been worked for flint in weapons and tools. Another early mining operation was the turquoise mine operated by the ancient Egyptians at Wady Maghareh on the Sinai Peninsula. Turquoise was also mined in pre-Colombian America in the Cerillos mining district in New Mexico, where a mass of rock 200 feet in depth and 300 feet in width was removed with stone tools. The resulting mine dump of unusable rock covers 20 acres. Gemstones are generally obtained by alluvial or host rock mining.

Alluvial mining

By far, the most common method of mining gemstones, alluvial mining, is the extraction of gems from sedimentary deposits, also known as *placer* or *secondary deposits*.

They are called secondary deposits because the gems are not found in the rock in which they formed or are hosted, but in deposits caused by the weathering and erosion of primary deposits. It includes the prospecting of riverbeds (i.e., the water flow is dammed so the less dense clay and sand are swept away—the remaining gem gravel is then agitated so the gems can be extracted and sorted) or the mining of gems from sedimentary deposits located beneath the earth's surface (i.e., the digging of pits, vertical shafts, and tunnels to reach gem gravels). Examples of alluvial mining include river and shaft mining in Ratnapura, Sri Lanka, and Ilakaka,

Madagascar. A variation of alluvial mining is marine mining, which is the mining of sandy coastal strata by dredging (e.g., amber from Kaliningrad, Russia).

Typically, a miner will dig using either hand tools (on a small-scale mine) or heavy industrial machinery. The earth is then taken to be washed either by hand or with the aid of machinery. This is exactly how it sounds—the loose earth is washed with water to get rid of the debris, leaving gemstones in the *wash*. This wash is then trawled through to find the rough gemstones. It is an incredibly laborious and time-consuming process that can, from day to day, yield very little. Typically, only a few little gems remain at the end of washing and sorting.

Alluvial deposits tend to include more than one gem type and this can be useful, as the presence of one gem type can often indicate the presence of another. Such gems are called *tracers*, as they allow prospectors to trace down other varieties. Other methods of prospecting include the mapping of ancient riverbeds and streams.

Although gem crystals from alluvial deposits tend to be rounded, scratched, and cracked due to the weathering processes they have endured, this is actually beneficial, as the culling of poorer specimens has already occurred. In fact, the percentage of gem-quality crystals found in alluvial deposits is generally higher than those obtained from primary host rock deposits.

Host rock mining
Also known as *primary deposits, host rock mining* is the chipping of gems from the rock in which they formed or are hosted. Crystals from these deposits are extracted from their host rock by hand tools, pneumatic tools, and even explosives. Performed for centuries, this mining is typically done by digging underground tunnels. In some cases, gemstones can be harvested directly

JTV videographer Ryan Acree, the mine owner, and a miner descend into Block D.

from underground caves (e.g., the mining of moonstone from limestone caves near the village of Kangayam in Tamil Nadu, southern India).

Depending on the hardness of the primary material, host rock mining can either be comparatively easy (e.g., mining of kunzite from pegmatites at Betafo, Madagascar) or extremely difficult (e.g., mining of tanzanite from metamorphic rocks at the Merelani Foothills in northern Tanzania).

While some gems are easily removed by picks or drills, sometimes the host material must be crushed before the gems can be extracted and sorted for quality. At many diamond mines, they use *grease tables*. This is a method of diamond extraction whereby crushed rock is run down a gently sloping table covered in grease. Because diamonds are *hydrophobic* (water repellent), any diamonds present in the sample will adhere to the grease.

A lot of work for a little beauty—two days' yield from a sapphire mine near Ilakaka, Madagascar

The rarity of gems

Imagine sitting for hours in the sweltering Brazilian bush, watching two miners muscle spade after spade of earth out of an ever-deeper hole. Getting up to leave, you take stock of the day's finds—one small colorless topaz and an equally small aquamarine.

Consider the labor of a group of artisinal miners in Madagascar. When their production from the past two days' work is displayed, the tiny pile of stones does not fill even half a palm. At a nearby mechanized mine, despite machinery and a crew of a dozen, cleaning out the jig yields just a few dozen sapphires, none of which will cut a stone above two carats.

These, as well as many similar events throughout the world, drive home the true rarity of fine colored stones (not to mention the difficulty often encountered in bringing them to market). Perhaps Walter Huston put it best in the classic movie, *The Treasure of the Sierra Madre*:

Why is gold worth some twenty bucks an ounce? A thousand men, say, go searchin' for gold. After six months, one of them's lucky.... His find represents not only his own labor, but that of 999 others, to boot. That's 6000 months, 500 years, scramblin' over a mountain, goin' hungry and thirsty. An ounce of gold, mister, is worth what it is because of the human labor that went into the findin' and the gettin' of it.

When you purchase a precious gem, you own one of nature's rarest creations. So much of nature's beauty is ephemeral, passing quickly away. Gems are among the most enduring examples of the natural world and, arguably, the most beautiful, too.

GEMSTONE CUTTING

Cutting is not a single process, but a series of processes that takes nature's raw material, known as *rough*, and transforms it into something of even greater beauty—a gemstone. Cutting is a balance of art and science.

Slicing

Pre-forming

Shaping

Polishing

Unlike diamonds, colored gems possess variable optical properties; therefore, they cannot be cut to a fixed, uniform standard. Lapidaries (gemstone cutters) have to take various factors into consideration when exercising their skills (e.g., cleavage, hardness, pleochroism, internal characteristics). A well-cut gemstone needs to balance yield (maximum weight) with beauty.

In general, a well-cut gemstone should have uniform color distribution, good brilliance (the proper blend of proportions, symmetry, and finish), and an acceptable number of inclusions. In addition, the majority of its carat weight should not be below the girdle, where it cannot be seen (small outline top down, but deep belly).

Broadly, gemstones are fashioned in one of two ways: faceted or cut *en cabochon*. The former consists of geometrically shaped, polished surfaces. The surfaces are commonly flat, but may also be concave (inwardly curved). Gemstones cut *en cabochon* generally have a flat bottom and a domed top (without facets). In some cases, the bottom may also be convex, but the dome is not as high. Gems fashioned en cabochon are called *cabs* and frequently described as *cabbed*.

The steps in faceting gemstones include:

Slicing Also called *sawing, slicing* is one of the most crucial stages in the initial transformation from rough to gemstone (if not the most crucial), as it will ultimately determine

CHOICE CUTS

Round brilliant cut

Barion cut

Step (emerald) cut

Mixed cut

Trilliant cut

Princess cut

Briolette cut

Cabochon cut

COMMON SHAPES

Round   Oval   Pear   Marquise   Heart

Square   Square Emerald   Square Cushion   Baguette   Tapered Baguette

Rectangle   Emerald   Cushion   Triangle

Top view (crown) Bottom view (pavilion)

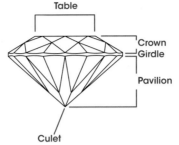

Table

Crown
Girdle

Pavilion

Table

Table

Culet

Culet

Parts of a faceted gem

the size, shape, and, to some degree, beauty of the finished gem. For this process, the gem slicer uses a diamond-tipped circular steel saw. Once the rough is selected, the gem slicer must consider how and where to cut. After this determination is made, he has to decide how many pieces to cut, as well as the shape of each piece. The goal is to produce the highest quality with an acceptable loss of weight. If the rough is cut incorrectly, its beauty may be diminished, relegating an exceptional gem to the ordinary.

Preforming Once the rough has been carefully sliced into optimal shapes and sizes (uniform or elongated cubes), preforming begins. This process requires tremendous experience and concentration. Preformers carry a great responsibility since they determine both shape and orientation for each gemstone; mistakes at this stage can be catastrophic. Apart from beauty, preformers always bear in mind the weight of the finished gem. Preforming is typically performed by using a vertical steel grinding wheel.

Shaping The shaper uses a special type of heat-activated resin to affix the preformed gemstone onto a metal rod, commonly called a *dop stick*. The shaper then delicately applies the gemstone to the shaping wheel to obtain a more accurate presentation of the size and facets. Due to the immense precision required by this process, the shaper is usually a very experienced preformer. Shaping is completed using a hand-operated shaping wheel.

Polishing The final step is known as polishing. Once gemstones have reached their ideal size and shape, they are taken to a steel (or steel and copper) horizontal polishing wheel for the final stage of their transformation. A polisher completes the faceting and applies the final polish using a fine diamond paste to produce a mirror-like surface. This final stage is responsible for unleashing the full brilliance and fire of a gemstone.

While gem cutters can become proficient with a few months' training, it may take many years to become a skilled preformer.

In general, the shape of a gem largely depends on the original shape of the rough (as nature created it) or the handiwork of a slicer. The oval shape is most frequently used, as it best balances beauty and carat weight retention. Factors to consider when choosing to facet a gem in another shape include design aesthetics, inclusions, carat weight loss, and color.

It is important to note that shape and cut are two different aspects of a gem. An oval-shaped gemstone, for example, may have a modified brilliant, flower, or mixed step cut. Cut refers to the style of faceting, which is modified by the shape, placement, quantity, size, and number of mirror-like surfaces on the exterior of a gem. There are many styles of cutting for the various shapes of gems. Some of the more popular include the following:

Brilliant cut

The brilliant cut is standard for round diamonds and typically has 57 facets (58 if a culet is present). It is often modified for use in colored stones. Although no single person has officially been credited with its invention, a Venetian cutter by the name of Vincenzo Peruzzi is often acknowledged for introducing a seminal version of the brilliant cut in the latter part of the 1680s. His style was "squarish" in appearance but had 57 to 58 facets.

The modern brilliant cut is the result of the work of a number of individuals in the late 19th and early 20th centuries, most prominently Henry Morse and Marcel Tolkowsky. Through both practical experiments and theoretical suppositions, the

Round brilliant cut

proportions necessary to create the best balance of brilliance, dispersion, and scintillation (play of light) were calculated. While these "ideal proportions" are important in the diamond trade, they are much less so with colored gems, even when cut in the brilliant style. This is because colored stone lapidaries must pay greatest attention to color, as opposed to maximizing factors like brilliance or dispersion.

The brilliant style of cutting is extremely flexible, and today, it is applied to a variety of shapes other than round (e.g., pear, oval, cushion, marquise, heart). The angles, shapes, and sizes of various facets are often modified to maximize the optical properties of each species or variety of gemstone.

Step (emerald) cut

Another prominent style of cutting employs stepped, trapezoidal facets; hence, the name *trap step, trap,* or *step cut.* It is commonly used on square- or rectangular-shaped gems, frequently with short, cut corners (creating 8 sides). This reduces the risk of chipping or fracture during the process of setting. The step cut's long, unbroken facets also display the gem's color to maximum advantage. However, this cutting style works best with relatively clean or richly colored material since inclusions are more noticeable,

The step cut was developed specifically for emeralds, to reduce the amount of pressure exerted during cutting and to protect the

Step or emerald cut

gemstones from chipping. This style was seen so frequently that many people started describing it as an *emerald cut.* Today, modern cutting techniques make this less important, but the style is popularly used for a wide variety of gem types.

Mixed cut

The cutting style most often used for rubies, sapphires, and other colored gems is the *mixed cut* (or *mixed step cut*), so called because it combines a brilliant cut crown with a step cut pavilion. Its chief advantage lies in the fact that the cutter can retain as much weight as possible by rounding off the steps, or facet rows, on the pavilion. This extra weight retention, however, does not come without a price. If the facet rows nearest the girdle are cut too steep, extinction is created, with light passing out the side instead of returning to the eyes as brilliance.

Mixed cut

Barion cut

Developed by South African diamond cutter Basil Watermeyer in the latter part of 1970, barion cuts allow adaptation of the round brilliant style of pavilion facets to angular shapes, such as the emerald, square emerald, kite, triangle, pentagon, and hexagon. Their key features are half-moon-shaped pavilion facets at the girdle, which allow brilliant-style facets to be placed upon angular-shaped stones. The crown is cut in the standard step-cut style. Barion cuts produce as much or more brilliance than even the standard round brilliant cut, as well as greater weight retention. Unlike step cuts, barions do not allow rounding of the pavilion (which gives greater freedom in weight retention).

Barion cut

Princess cut

The princess cut was an innovation that strove to maximize the brilliance, fire, and sparkle of square-shaped diamonds. The princess also had the added benefit of increased yield from octahedral diamond crystals, making princess-cut diamonds more affordable than a round brilliant cut of similar quality and weight.

Prior to the advent of this style, square or rectangular diamonds were generally step cut. The Quadrillion™, a successor to the princess cut, made further improvements on a good design. Some of the more notable characteristics of a princess cut are the chevrons on the pavilion of the stone. There are usually 2, 3, or 4, which are wider at the bottom and taper to a point at the corners. On round brilliant cuts, the main pavilion facets are wider on top and taper to a point at the bottom (culet).

Princess cut

Although initially developed for diamond, the princess cut was soon applied to colored stones, which also benefit from improved brilliance and sparkle. The princess cut is most notable when used on lighter colored, transparent gems.

Trillion and trilliant cuts

Although both names are often used interchangeably, the trillion cut was a precursor to the trilliant. Developed by Leon Finker, the trillion was originally designed to maximize the fire, brilliance, sparkle, and yield from triangular-shaped diamond rough (called *macles*). The trilliant, developed by Milton and Irving Meyer, was another style of triangular brilliant that was designed for the same purpose. Of the two terms, *trillion* is more frequently used in the gem trade.

Trilliant cut

Both styles of cutting have been modified for use on colored stones. Variations of the style may produce triangular gems with straight or curved sides, although the latter is much more common. Triangular gems with curved sides generally have thicker tips than those found on their straight-sided counterparts. Thicker tips give gemstones improved durability during setting.

In general, trillions are good for improving the brilliance, fire, and sparkle of lighter gemstones. However, trillions can also be used to great effect on darker gems. The pavilion, which is shallower than that on most styles of cutting, has the added benefit of making darker gems lighter and livelier.

Briolette cut

Briolette cut

The briolette is an older style of faceting that falls into the category of antique cuts, possibly dating back as far as the 12th century. It is considered a modification of the double rose cut, in which one half has been elongated.

In general, briolettes have cylindrical, teardrop shapes. They can range from stubby and bulbous to long and slender. Facets are commonly triangular but may be rhomboid or even kite shaped. Briolettes have no crown, table, or pavilion and no fixed number of facets.

It is thought that the famous French traveler and trader Jean-Baptiste Tavernier brought briolettes back from India during one of his long voyages to the Orient. Briolettes enjoyed considerable popularity during the Victorian, Edwardian, and Art Deco periods. That appeal can still be seen in the form of antique tiaras, necklaces, and earrings, as well as many estate pieces.

The popularity of briolettes is once again on the rise, making them featured items in many jewelry and gem publications, as well as fashion magazines such as *Vogue* and *Harper's Bazaar*. They can be found in precious metals such as gold, silver, and platinum, but are rapidly gaining momentum in fashion jewelry. The briolette offers a unique blend of history, elegance, and beauty.

Cabochon cut

The word *cabochon* is derived from the old Norman French word *caboche*, meaning *head*. A cabochon is a polished gemstone with a flat bottom (or slightly rounded bottom) and a convex or rounded domed top. This style contains no facets. The traditional cabochon is an oval, but cabochons can also be fashioned into other shapes such as rounds, triangles, and rectangles.

Cabochon cut

Cabochon, commonly known as *cab*, is the oldest and most common form of gem cutting. Gems cut en *cabochon* are shaped and polished rather than cut. In antiquity, this was generally the only cutting option available other than using the gem with the natural facets of its crystal structure. Some of the most beautiful ancient jewelry was made with cabochons, including that of India and the breastplate of Aaron.

Cabochons are used for making jewelry, often carved as *intaglio* (a gem carved in negative relief) or *cameo* (a gem carved in positive relief), and are also used in crystal healing. Today, the cabochon cut is applied to gems of limited transparency (e.g., turquoise, jade, agate) or as a result of predominant inclusions (e.g., relatively opaque sapphires, rubies, or emeralds) or for gems that have special optical properties (e.g., asterism, chatoyancy, iridescence). In the latter case, the domed surface of the cab is needed to maximize the visual effect of the phenomenon.

Buff-top cut

Buff-top cut

The buff top is a hybrid style that incorporates elements of a cabochon with those of a faceted gemstone. It is used to good effect on transparent material. The buff top has a domed (cabbed) crown and a faceted pavilion. The dome often acts as a magnifier. It can be used to highlight special internal characteristics or simply enhance the illusion of depth when viewing the stone through the crown. This style of cut shows improved brilliance due to the pavilion facets and provides greater durability since the smooth surface of the domed crown is less easily abraded.

Concave cut

The concave cut has taken the gemstone industry by storm. It is an innovative style that employs an inwardly curved, conical-shaped facet. This contrasts with the two-dimensional style of traditional flat facets. The additional dimension of depth creates more brilliance in lower RI gems and distributes light more evenly. Gemstones sporting a concave cut often give the impression that light is flowing through the stones. Visually, many gems benefit from a softer, richer interior glow.

Concave cut

A concave cut may be applied to the top or bottom of a gem (crown and pavilion) or used on both. Concave faceting requires specialized equipment and a higher degree of skill. This style of cut is best suited to lighter, transparent gem materials. Concave-cut gemstones are generally more expensive than traditional cuts since inwardly curved facets realize lower yield (weight retention) from rough and require additional time and labor for completion.

Flower cut

Flower cut

This cut is commonly used on many gemstones. The name is an allusion to the pattern of facets on the pavilion and crown of a stone, which creates the impression of overlapping petals. This cut is frequently used on tanzanite, providing excellent brilliance and good weight retention. The flower cut is a variation on the *old Portuguese cut*, and the two terms are often used interchangeably.

Mirror cut

The mirror cut is notable for its exceptionally large table and generally simple style of faceting. The effect in some gems, such as the historical diamond *Miroir du Portugal*, gives the impression of an extended bellows, or a hall of mirrors, leading to infinity. In this case, the dimension of depth or distance is created by a limited number of stepped, trapezoidal facets on the pavilion.

A simplified mirror cut is an excellent choice for highlighting the presence of interesting internal characteristics such as needles or dendrites. The large table acts as a window into the heart of the stone and allows a cutter to emphasize nature's internal treasures. JTV has used the mirror cut to highlight the presence of rutile and tourmaline needles encapsulated in quartz (called, respectively, *rutilated* and *tourmalinated* quartz), but you will see many other special gem varieties taking advantage of this cut.

Mirror cut Miroir du Portugal
Replica from
www.museumdiamonds.com

Baguette cut

This style borrows its name from a French term meaning *rod*, which, as you may note, brings to mind a similarly shaped loaf of bread by the same name. Baguettes are often rectangular in shape but may be tapered on one end. Most baguette diamonds have 14 facets, but variations occur. Generally, the length is 1.5 times greater than the width, but the ratio has some degree of variability.

Baguettes are most frequently seen in diamonds, but are also found in the realm of colored stones. Commonly used as an accent to larger stones, the baguette is also well suited

Baguette cut

to a channel setting with its straight sides. When channel set, baguettes seemingly form a river of color. It is rare to see baguettes in excess of 1ct. Most are smaller sizes to complement or contrast with a central diamond or colored stone.

Fantasy cut

This highly personal and specialized creation places no limits on shape, style, or any other aspect of a gem. Fantasy cuts may incorporate elements of concave and traditional faceting, as well as drilling and hand or laser carving. The surfaces of a gem may be polished, frosted, etched, or even left natural, expressing the skill and creativity of the lapidary. Fantasy cuts are often applied to rough that is unusual in shape, although pieces may be symmetrical when finished. Most fantasy cuts are one-of-a-kind creations, and due to the high degree of skill and labor involved, are poorly suited to mass production.

Fantasy cut

Many of the world's finest fantasy cuts come from Idar-Oberstein, a medieval town in Germany with an international reputation for innovation, excellence, and creativity in the fashioning of gemstones.

Fancy cut

Fancy cut

As mentioned previously, shape and cut are two different aspects of gemstones. When discussing shapes, the term *fancy* will often be heard. In terms of diamonds and colored stones, any shape other than a round is considered a fancy shape. This may seem like a very one-sided proposition, but it is simple in concept.

Common fancy shapes include oval, octagon (square and rectangular), pear, heart, marquise (or navette), trillion, and cushion. However, if you want something truly different, there are flowers, stars, kites, chevrons, lunettes (half-moons), cloverleaves, and many other exotic fancy shapes available. Jewelry Television endeavors to bring many of these to our viewing audience.

The important fact to remember is that this ever-widening choice of shapes and designs is being created to suit a variety of individual styles and tastes. No single cut or shape is more beautiful than another. The magic of nature and the artistry of the cutter combine to make each a unique work of art.

GEMSTONE TREATMENTS

Skillfully merging art and science, a variety of techniques is used to help gemstones reach their full potential. Just as critical as good cutting, enhancements (treatments) are an integral part of the modern gemstone industry.

Jewels have been objects of desire from the earliest days of mankind. The enduring value of gems and pearls is largely a result of their beauty, durability, and rarity. It is this last aspect that has pushed humans to create less expensive alternatives to the natural product. These include imitations such as glass, fully synthetic counterparts of natural gems, and enhancements that modify gems and pearls to make them more valuable.

Certain enhancements have been practiced for literally thousands of years. The dying of agate is one example. Others, such as irradiated blue topaz, are solely a product of the technological advances of the modern age.

Enhancements have a definite impact on the value of precious stones, with the highest prices paid for natural gems of fine quality that have not been enhanced in any way beyond ordinary cutting and polishing. As a gem is modified to a greater and greater degree, the change in value is also greater. The least expensive gems are those fully made by man (synthetics) because the supply is essentially unlimited. Thus, they have limited or no rarity.

Basic definitions
Generally, gemstones can be placed into one of two broad categories: natural or artificial. In some cases, natural and artificial gem materials may be combined into an assembled piece such as a doublet or triplet. Included below are a few short definitions to clarify some commonly used terms:

Natural Any gem material, organic or inorganic, that forms without the intervention of man. By strict definition, natural gems only undergo the standard process of cutting and polishing.

Natural enhanced A natural gem whose appearance has been improved by a standard industry treatment (e.g., heating of ruby, citrine, and tanzanite). These do not require disclosure since the enhancement does not create any substantial difference in value or any special care requirements.

Natural treated Some natural gems are enhanced by methods that go well beyond those considered standard by the industry. These treatments may create special-care requirements and/or a substantial difference in the perceived value of a gem. Such treatments must always be disclosed (e.g., CVD topaz, fissure-filled ruby, irradiated diamond, lattice-diffused sapphire).

| Natural | Natural enhanced (Heated) | Natural treated (CVD) |

Artificial	Synthetic	Natural pearl	Cultured pearl
Yellow YAG	Strontium titanate		

Artificial This designation is the catch-all for any gems or gem materials that are man-made, or created through the intervention of man. Some artificial gems have no analog in nature (e.g., yttrium aluminum garnet [YAG], gadolinium gallium garnet [GGG]).

Synthetic This is a specific sub-category of artificial. A man-made (lab-created) gem material must fulfill two criteria for the designation *synthetic*. First, it must have a natural analog; second, it must have the same chemical, optical, and physical properties as its natural counterpart. Examples include synthetic sapphire, ruby, and emerald.

Natural pearl Rarely seen in the jewelry trade, natural pearls are created through an organic process without any intervention by man. Whenever the term *pearl* is used without a modifier, it refers to the naturally occurring variety.

Cultured pearl Although formed by the same process as their natural counterparts, cultured pearls are products of human intervention and cannot be considered "natural." With rare exceptions, all South Sea, Akoya, and Tahitian pearls sold by JTV are cultured. JTV also sells a wide variety of cultured freshwater pearls.

Imitation This is any material, natural or artificial, that has the appearance of another generally more valuable gem material. Appearance is where the similarity ends. Red glass, for example, is a common imitation for ruby.

—————— **Diamond Simulants** ——————

Synthetic	Natural	Synthetic	Artificial
Cubic zirconia	Zircon	Moissanite	YAG

Simulant This is any gem material, natural or artificial, that is generally used as a substitute for another more valuable gem. This term can be used interchangeably with *imitation*. Synthetic red cubic zirconia, red glass, and natural red garnet all qualify as ruby simulants.

Doublet
Aussie opal

Triplet
Aussie opal

Assembled This is composed of two or more gem materials using a bonding agent. The most common assembled gems are *doublets* and *triplets*. The component parts may be all natural, artificial, or a combination of natural and artificial gems. Assembled gems offer an affordable alternative to similar-looking, solid, or single-piece natural gems.

Doublet This is an assembled gem that consists of two pieces held together by a colorless bonding agent. Common examples include opal and quartz doublets.

Triplet This is an assembled gem that consists of three gem materials held together by a colorless bonding agent or two gem materials and a colored bonding agent (the colored bonding agent considered a third component). Common examples include opal and quartz triplets.

Reconstructed
Pressed amber

Hybrid
Mahaleo Ruby™

Reconstructed This process makes use of heat, pressure, and/or solvents to fuse small pieces of a gem together into a single, larger whole. Pressed amber is a common example of a reconstructed gem.

Hybrid This is a gem with natural and artificial components, where the two cannot be separated. This term is designed to address a new generation of treatments that add artificial substances such as glass or polymers to the natural base material. This process generally improves the apparent clarity of the host but may also improve color.

Lab-created This term is used to describe any gem material synthesized by man. Lab-created gems may or may not have a natural counterpart (synthetic versus artificial).

Durability This is an important aspect of gemstones. Durability is a combination of three factors: hardness, toughness, and stability. Hardness is resistance to scratching, toughness is resistance to breakage, and stability is resistance to change in the presence of external factors such as light, heat, and chemicals.

Enhancement disclosure

Jewelry Television® takes treatment disclosure seriously and, to the best of our ability, provides our customers and viewers with complete information on any and all forms of enhancement. The treatment disclosures shown on our website (JTV.com) are based upon established industry standards and have been expanded to ensure greater accuracy and promote fuller understanding.

Some natural gems only undergo the basic process of cutting, polishing, and normal cleaning. These come to you as nature created them, without any enhancements. Other gems may undergo processes beyond normal cleaning, cutting, and polishing. This may be done to alter or improve color, improve some aspect of durability, or create a special optical property such as asterism. These gems are still natural but have been enhanced to some degree.

Jewelry Television discloses all enhancements that create special care requirements or substantially alter the value of a gem. When shown on broadcast, JTV® provides a special code to help identify the treatment. A more detailed description of this code is available on our website and is also printed on the JTV invoice accompanying your purchase. Examples of gemstones requiring disclosure include irradiated blue diamonds, CVD (chemical vapor deposition) topaz, and diffused sapphire.

Many gems may be enhanced by industry-accepted standards and are always assumed to be treated. Examples include heat-treated ruby, sapphire, tanzanite, and citrine. These treatments do not create special-care requirements or alter the value of your gem. Jewelry Television is not required to disclose these, but provides full information on all invoices and on our website at JTV.com.

Some gems, such as garnet, spinel, and peridot, are rarely enhanced and come to you as nature made them. In a few cases, where natural, untreated gems are rarely seen, JTV may note the difference in the gemstone description (e.g., unheated natural ruby or sapphire). These are the exception to the rules and are highlighted for the sake of clarity.

Since certain enhancements are undetectable or difficult to detect, Jewelry Television takes the position that any item is enhanced unless specific gemological evidence proves otherwise. Jewelry Television has taken an industry leadership role in the disclosure process and has established standard guidelines for the testing and verification of treatments. We also hold our vendors to a high level of accountability.

Jewelry Television does its best to describe our gems in a clear, consistent, and honest fashion. **Our approach is to give our customers the same information we would like if we were purchasing the piece.** Our mantra is to be true both to our customers and to the precious stones with which we are privileged to work.

Jewelry Television® Treatment Chart

In our effort to provide the most up-to-date information on gemstone treatments, Jewelry Television developed a chart that provides important details on a wide range of gems and gem materials. The chart is updated as new information becomes available and is always viewable at JTV.com through our *Learning Library.* The basic format is as follows:

Gemstone/Types	Hardness	Enhancement Method(s)	Purpose	Frequency	Stability/Durability	Care and Handling

Gemstone/types

This list is alphabetical and generally provides information by species first, then varieties within each species where pertinent. Beryl, for example, will include variety names such as aquamarine, bixbite, emerald, goshenite, heliodor, and morganite. You will also find any variety described solely by color (e.g., green beryl) or phenomenon (e.g., star sapphire).

Hardness

This column describes the degree of scratch resistance for each mineral or gemstone. Hardness is a relative scale ranging from 1 to 10, with 10 (diamond) being the hardest. The scale was devised in 1812 by Friedrich Mohs, a German mineralogist. The 10 original minerals were (softest to hardest): talc, gypsum, calcite, fluorite, apatite, orthoclase, quartz, topaz, corundum, and diamond. Any unknown material that can be scratched by a mineral on the Mohs' scale must be softer than that mineral. The converse is also true.

Enhancement method(s)

There are many methods used to treat gem materials. In some cases, more than one type of treatment may produce similar results in color or clarity. These will both be listed individually. In other cases, a combination of two treatments may be used to produce a desired result (e.g., irradiation [color] and heating [stabilization] of diamond). Corresponding enhancement codes are also listed in this column.

Purpose

This column clarifies the purpose of treatments. Treatments may be used to alter or improve color, improve clarity, or create some type of optical phenomenon. In some cases, a treatment may serve two purposes (e.g., improve appearance and stabilize a gem).

Frequency

Frequency relates to how often a treatment is applied to a specific gem material. This generally falls into one of four categories: rarely, occasionally, frequently, or always.

Stability/durability

Some gems, after treatment, may be less stable than others. This means that the appearance may change with exposure to various external factors such as heat, light, and chemicals. Jewelry Television rates the permanence of enhancements on the following scale: poor, fair, good, very good, and excellent. In some cases, a range may be given (fair to good, good to excellent). A few treatments may be so new that it is impossible to accurately determine stability. If this is the case, Jewelry Television will state "research in progress." An enhancement is considered stable if the appearance of a gem does not change under normal wear, cutting, cleaning, repair, or display conditions.

Care and handling

This column provides additional information about enhancements and general guidelines for handling. If a treatment creates special-care requirements, it is noted here. Even natural (untreated) gems may require special consideration during wear, cleaning, or repair. Jewelry Television provides this information so that you may enjoy and prolong the beauty of your gemstones.

Enhancement codes and descriptions

The following chart contains enhancement codes, the full name of each enhancement, and a basic description.

CODE	NAME	DESCRIPTION
BL	Bleached	The use of heat, light, and/or chemicals or other agents to lighten or remove a gemstone's color. This process is sometimes accompanied by subsequent dying and/or impregnation to stabilize the resulting color.
CTD	Coated	The use of surface enhancements such as lacquering, enameling, inking, foiling, or sputtering of films to improve appearance or durability, provide color, or add other special effects.
CVD	CVD Coated	Chemical vapor deposition is a high-tech process for coating gems. It is commonly applied to the entire exterior of stones to change or improve color or to create new and unusual special effects.
DIF	Channel/Pipe Diffusion*	A high-temperature diffusion of coloring elements, such as copper, along certain channels in feldspars.
DYED	Dyed/Stained	The introduction of coloring matter into a gemstone to give it a new color, intensify an existing color, or improve uniformity of color.
FF	Fracture Filled	The filling of surface-reaching cavities or fissures with colorless glass, plastic, resin, or some similar substance. This process may improve appearance, durability, and/or weight.
FF	Lead Glass Filled	A low-temperature process used to fill surface-reaching cavities or fissures with leaded glass. This treatment is a less durable form of fracture filling. It is commonly used to improve appearance but may also add weight.
FH	Flux Healed	A treatment that heals fractures or fissures by applying heat and flux or heat alone. The process dissolves the interior walls of the host and re-deposits molten gem material, which heals the fractures closed.
HE	Heated	The application of heat to improve the appearance of a gemstone. This process may alter color, clarity, and/or phenomena.
HPHT	High Pressure/ High Temperature	The combined application of heat and pressure to affect desired alterations of color and/or clarity.
IMP	Impregnated	The impregnation of a porous gem material with a colorless agent (usually plastic or wax) to give it greater durability and improve appearance.
LAS	Lasered	The use of a laser and chemicals to reach and alter inclusions, making them less noticeable.

CODE	NAME	DESCRIPTION
IRR	Irradiation	The use of neutron, gamma, ultraviolet, and/or electron bombardment to alter a gemstone's color. Irradiation may be followed by an annealing (heating) process.
DIF	Surface Diffusion	The outside-in diffusion of elements via high-temperature heat treatment to produce a thin layer of color and/or asterism.
DIF	Lattice Diffusion	The outside-in diffusion of elements via high-temperature heat treatment. This process also alters color but penetrates more deeply.
INF	Infused with Oil, Resin, etc.	The filling of surface-reaching fissures with colorless oil, resin, or other colorless substance, excluding glass or plastic, to improve a gemstone's appearance.
PVD	PVD Coated	Physical vapor deposition produces a coating that is applied to the surface of a product. The coating is then sealed with a polymer to protect it.
SM	Smoked	In the smoke treatment process, the opals are wrapped in silver foil paper and heated. The smoke penetrates the opal and darkens the background color. This process results in a brighter play of color since the background is darkened.
STB	Stabilized	This process employs colorless wax or resin to fill tiny gaps within a host material, improving durability and protecting the host from discoloration. Stabilization does not add color, but color may improve as a byproduct of the treatment.
SA	Sugar Acid	The sugar-acid treatment is a two-step process that is used on certain porous gem materials such as matrix opal. Heating in a sugar-saturated solution is followed by immersion in a concentrated acid bath. The reaction between sugar and acid leaves carbon, which darkens the background and highlights the play of color.
W or O	Waxed or Oiled	The impregnation of a porous gem with colorless wax, paraffin, and/or oil to improve appearance.

CARING FOR YOUR GEMS & JEWELRY

Gems are among the most durable of nature's creations but still require care if they are to retain their beauty. Caring for your jewelry is a matter of common sense and simple precaution:

- Choose your method of cleaning based on the softest or most vulnerable component in your jewelry. If you have an emerald and diamond ring, for example, the emerald, and not the diamond, should govern the cleaning method.
- Check your jewelry for loose stones by gently shaking or tapping it next to your ear. Have any loose gems properly tightened by your jeweler prior to wearing.
- Check clasps and fasteners often to make sure they are secure. If you are unsure, have a local jeweler check your piece.
- Restring all bead and pearl necklaces every two years or sooner if worn regularly. Bead and pearl necklaces should have knots between each gem.
- Remove your jewelry before engaging in activities such as sports, housework, or gardening.
- Put jewelry on after using lotions, cosmetics, hair spray, or perfumes (never before).
- Never remove your jewelry by pulling on the gems.
- Carefully wipe jewelry with a soft, lint-free cloth after each wearing to remove oils and salts.
- Store each piece of jewelry separately. Use compartments in jewelry boxes or store individually in pouches.
- Store necklaces flat so that the harder stones do not scratch the softer ones, or so the gemstones do not scratch the metal. Almost every gem is harder than the metal in which it is set.
- Clean your jewelry on occasion with a jewelry-cleaning solution or mechanical cleaner suitable for the gems. When in doubt, use warm soapy water and a soft toothbrush.
- Clean your gems over a bowl and not the sink (unless you enjoy plumbing).
- Think twice before putting gems in an ultrasonic cleaner. Diamonds, rubies, and sapphires are generally fine, but many other gems may not be. When in doubt, leave it out!
- Porous, opaque gems such as lapis lazuli, turquoise, and malachite require special care. These gems may absorb chemicals and soap, so they should just be gently wiped clean with a moist cloth.
- Opals also require special care. Never use an ultrasonic cleaner or ammonia, and avoid heat or strong light that can dry out the water in opals.
- Organic gems like pearl, coral, and amber should only be wiped clean with a moist cloth. Due to their organic nature, these gems are both soft and porous. Avoid contact with hair sprays, cosmetics, or perfume to prolong their beauty.
- Some natural and certain color-enhanced gems may fade with prolonged exposure to sunlight. Do not leave these on a windowsill or a display case exposed to direct sunlight. This includes dyed agates and dyed pearls.
- Do not use the same cloth to clean all your gems. The cloth that you use for your sapphires, rubies, and diamonds, for example, may contain particles that can scratch softer gems, such as apatite or tanzanite.
- If you want to make a piece of jewelry with your favorite gemstone, consider its durability. Softer gems are better suited to earrings and pendants, as are treated gems with certain special-care requirements.
- Gemstones softer than a seven on the Mohs' scale of hardness are more susceptible to scratching, since quartz dust is abundantly present in the air we breathe. Blow off any dust prior to cleaning with a soft, lint-free cloth.

Mechanical cleaners

The most common mechanical cleaners are ultrasonic and steam cleaners.

Ultrasonic cleaners feature two basic parts: a small motor and a cleaning tank filled with either water or a chemical cleaning solution. The machine's motor produces vibrating energy waves (an acoustic field—generally 20-40,000 waves per second) to create microscopic bubbles in the cleaning fluid tank. Called *non-inertial cavitation*, the motion created by collapsing bubbles knocks dirt off the jewelry and is effective in penetrating the tiny crevices that traditional cleaning cloths and topical cleaners cannot easily reach.

Mechanical cleaners, such as the ultrasonic unit above, should be used with caution because they can damage certain gems.

Ultrasonic cleaners produce heat, so they are not an option for heat-sensitive gems. In addition, heavily included gems should never be placed in an ultrasonic unit. The vibrations may accentuate fractures and cause damage.

A steam cleaner uses jets of steam to literally blast dirt off jewelry. It is effective in removing dirt from hard-to-reach places. Because heat is involved, steam cleaners should also never be used on heat-sensitive gems.

As mechanical cleaners can damage some gemstones, always check to see if your gem is suitable for such cleaning. When in doubt, avoid mechanical cleaners.

Chemical cleaners

Some gems are highly resistant to chemicals, while others are not. Thus, commercial jewelry cleaners should only be used when you are sure they will not damage the gems in question. Porous gems such as malachite, pearls, and turquoise should never be cleaned with chemicals. Filled gems, such as oiled emeralds or glass-filled rubies, may also suffer damage when exposed to chemical cleaners. Silver polish and ammonia can damage many gems. Commercial jewelry cleaners often contain ammonia, so be careful. When in doubt, do not use chemical cleaners.

Toothpaste is another no-no. It may contain abrasives that can scratch softer gems.

Diamonds and grease

Unlike other gems, diamonds are extremely hydrophobic, meaning they are repelled by water. The flipside to this property is that diamonds attract both grease and soap. This means that diamonds require more frequent cleaning to look their best. Take off your diamond-set jewelry to avoid the buildup of grit and soap prior to washing your hands and periodically clean it. While ultrasonic cleaning is safe for most diamonds, it should not be used with coated diamonds.

In conclusion

Gemstones are among the most durable of all natural materials and, when properly cared for, should retain their beauty for hundreds or even thousands of years. Even porous aggregates, such as lapis lazuli and turquoise, can last for millennia, as witnessed by pieces dating back 5,000 years or more.

Please remember: in order to keep your gems looking their best, you must treat them right. When in doubt, treat your gems as you would your own skin. Mild soap and a gentle scrubbing with a soft brush, followed by drying with a towel or cloth, are all that is needed to keep your gems looking beautiful for years to come.

THE GEM SUPPLY CHAIN

The colored-gem industry supply chain is long and tortuous—far longer than that of diamond. It is not uncommon for a gemstone to pass through seven intermediaries from the mine to the consumer.

By any industry standard, this is an extremely long and inefficient supply chain. Although the price keeps going up, other than at the cutting and setting stages, there is no real value being added to the gem.

On its passage through so many intermediaries, it is not uncommon for a colored gemstone to increase in price by up to ten times. For example, this means a $200 tanzanite from Tanzania may end up selling for $2,000 in the jeweler's window, and this does not even include the other jewelry components. Once you factor in labor, gold, and diamonds, the tanzanite that started at $200 could end up retailing in a shop window for a whopping $4,000.

At Jewelry Television, our goal is to remove as many intermediaries as possible. Our senior buyers have extensive gem trade experience and understand the true nature of the colored-stone pipeline from mine to finished product. It is through this knowledge base and our substantial network of contacts that we can provide a wide variety of gemstones and gem materials at the best value possible.

Jay Boyle and Jerry Sisk buy tanzanite rough in Arusha.

JEWELRY MAKING

JEWELRY MAKING

Jewelry Television® offers handcrafted jewelry creations in both silver (.925 sterling) and gold (10Kt, 14Kt, and 18Kt).

Gem cutting and gem matching

Completely reliant on the eyes and hands of skilled professionals, expert faceting and matching for size and color are critical in ensuring that the key ingredients in a gorgeous handcrafted piece of jewelry, the gems themselves, really shine. Before being set in jewelry, qualified professionals carefully examine each gem, separating them according to their clarity, color, cut, and carat weight. With satisfaction as our highest priority, JTV invests tremendous effort to ensure that only the highest quality gems are well matched before being set into a stunning array of handcrafted jewelry designs.

Jewelry design

Jewelry design is both an art and, surprisingly, a science. Inspiration and ideas come from the most unexpected sources. With a rich and varied color palette, using both hand-drawn and computer-aided design, our imaginative and creative design team fashions stunning jewelry creations to complement our gemstones.

Our jewelry design team regularly travels to the world's major jewelry markets in Asia, Europe, and the USA to stay abreast of the latest design and fashion trends. Jewelry Television has the expertise and flexibility to design high-quality, contemporary jewelry that is current with the latest European, global, and Hollywood fashions, as well as timeless pieces that embody classic design. Keeping you at the forefront of fashion, style, and beauty is a major goal at Jewelry Television.

Working hand in hand with our master model makers and jewelers, the JTV design team ensures that its creations are realized exactly how they were envisioned. The total process, from raw gold or silver to the finished product, includes many intermediate steps. The public does not often see these steps, but each requires skill and expertise in a specific aspect of jewelry manufacture.

Handmade jewelry

For individual pieces or smaller quantities, the jeweler literally starts with an amount of gold and then cuts, shapes, heats, and stretches it into the final jewelry. For larger quantities, we make an original masterpiece and then cast the required quantity of pieces from the master, finishing

Sorting stones

Designing jewelry

them all by hand. Many of the handcrafted pieces start from gold bars or grains. The jewelers are given the correct amount for the design, and then alloy is added to create 14Kt or 18Kt gold. The first step is to soften the gold to make it easier to craft. To do this, the jeweler uses an atmosphere control meter to heat the gold to a temperature of 1,877°F (1025°C).

For some designs, rather than starting with nuggets of gold, the jeweler starts with a length of gold that is already shaped into a round rod. The equipment we use to stretch the gold to the correct thickness is traditional, and the skills have been passed on through many generations. Once the gold has been heated and cut into a rough state, the jeweler then starts to shape the body of the piece. This art is fascinating to watch, as within minutes, you see a flat piece of gold transformed into jewelry by artisans whose only tools are their hammers and a wealth of experience.

Master model construction

When handcrafting larger quantities, we use a wax molding technique to construct the first step of a piece of jewelry. The master model-making workshop comprises two sections—silver model makers and wax carvers. Their expertise is diverse and includes everything from simple prong set and lightweight gemstone jewelry designs to artistically crafted masterpieces. These craftspeople are of critical importance, as their ability to turn a one-dimensional drawing into a three-dimensional master model is vital in ensuring that the finished jewelry exceeds all expectations. As with the old carpenter's adage—measure twice, cut once—all our master models must be exactingly precise, as any mistakes at this stage are going to appear in the finished jewelry.

Our designers, model makers, and jewelry teams work closely together to ensure the very best results are achieved.

Wax injection

The wax injection department comprises four sections: rubber mold making, wax injection, quality control and repair, and wax tree preparation. While the wax injection team carefully works with pre-set wax injection machines, the rubber mold makers understand the importance of correctly prepared rubber molds for improved wax injection. The quality control team ensures wax pieces are cleaned and in a proper condition for casting.

While all this sounds very complicated, the handcrafting process is actually very simple. From each drawing, we produce either a silver or wax master model. Once we have a master model, we make a mold of this using rubber. We then use these rubber molds to make multiple wax

A handmade ring starts to take form.

Master model construction

copies. Each is checked to be sure it is without defect. Remember, each of these will be a piece of handcrafted jewelry after casting—any mistakes here will show up in the finished design. Next, individual wax molds are affixed to a wax tree ready for casting.

Casting

Casting rooms include preparation facilities, curing ovens, vacuum casting, a high-water-pressure cleaning area, and wastewater disposal facilities. With the right experts controlling this process, the very best results are achieved, ensuring minimal complications for other processes later on. Again, like wax injection, the process itself is actually very simple.

Gem setters hard at work

The first step involves placing the wax tree in a cylinder and adding ceramic cement to form a shell around it. Once the shell has dried and hardened, the cylinders are heated until the wax melts out. The shell is then placed in an oven, and molten gold or silver is poured. With the assistance of a vacuum, the molten metal is pulled through the shell, filling every crevice. Once the metal cools and sets, the ceramic cement is cracked and cleaned away, leaving a casting tree.

Pre-finishing

Once the casting tree arrives at the pre-finishing stage, each individual casting is cut from the tree. This is jewelry in its raw, seminal form. At this point, specially trained craftsmen carefully prepare all the pieces, fully aware of the finishing needs for each individual design. Some pieces, such as gemstone rings or pendants, must be made ready for the setting stage. Others, like bracelets, must be hand assembled first. This may be done with a jeweler's torch or a high-tech laser, the latter providing superior strength and uniformity of welding in certain cases.

As with all stages involved in handcrafting jewelry, an embedded quality control team approves every handcrafted piece before it is transferred to the next stage.

Checking wax molds for quality

Pre-finishing a white gold ring

Gem setting

As the largest retailer of loose gemstones in the world, JTV features an extensive array of colored stones in its numerous handcrafted designs. The gem-setting stage requires carefully trained artisans who can handle many stones that are not commonly seen in the retail jewelry trade. Softer gems and those with special-care needs must be handled with the utmost skill. In some cases, these gems may require a more difficult style of setting, creating additional challenges for the craftsperson.

Quality control is always a major concern of JTV, so each piece is individually inspected before it is released to the next stage. JTV continuously ensures that the highest quality standards are met, while breaking new ground in both the types of setting and the gems within them.

Polishing and plating

At the polishing stage, we ensure that the best shine and finish are achieved but not at the expense of essential design details. This is done by carefully separating individual polishing needs. When plating is required, plating specialists apply a carefully calculated formula of rhodium or gold plating with an emphasis on both color and brightness.

Quality assurance

Quality assurance encompasses two areas. First, control teams check each step of the handcrafting process. Second, the final quality assurance after polishing takes place. The successful implementation of quality control teams minimizes and eliminates many problems. This is an important aspect of our handcrafted jewelry.

The final product approval is done by quality assurance professionals with years of experience in the creation of high-quality, handcrafted jewelry. By working closely with domestic and international quality control teams, JTV ensures that its quality standards meet or exceed expectations.

Jay Boyle inspects gemstones.

JEWELRY SETTINGS

JEWELRY SETTINGS

Most jewelry is crafted from individual components. The pieces are often created on the jeweler's bench and then skillfully joined together. The components needed in most types of jewelry are incredibly simple.

Even the most expensive "Tiffany-style" diamond ring features just three pieces—the band of the ring, the gallery that mounts the gem, and finally, the gem itself.

With a few peripheral components, such as earring posts, chains, and hinges (often known as *findings*), these basic components are used to make everything from solitaire and gem-set rings to earrings, necklaces, pendants, and more complex pieces. While the prong setting is the most frequently seen method of setting gems and diamonds, many other styles exist.

Prong setting

Also known as *claw setting*, this style employs small metal posts, called *prongs,* to secure a gemstone in place. Before setting, each prong must be modified. This process is known as *seating*. A small groove or notch is cut into the upper portion of each prong. This is where the girdle of the gemstone will reside. The top of the prongs above the notch become the tips, which are bent over the girdle and press against the crown facets. The tips are responsible for securely holding the gemstone in place.

Four- and six-prong settings are very popular for round and oval gems. The latter style is also known as a Tiffany setting because it was originally developed by the founder of Tiffany & Co. in 1886. Some gem shapes may be set in specialized "v-shaped" posts known as *chevron* prongs. These do a good job of protecting the thin tips of the stones. Chevron prongs are often used on marquise and triangular-shaped gems. Some shapes, such as pears and hearts, may use both standard and chevron prongs.

Another aspect of prongs is the style of tip. Tips may be fashioned into various shapes. Rounded, oval, and pointed tips are more common, but other possibilities exist. Sometimes tips are even formed into ornamental shapes, such as clovers or tridents. These highly specialized styles are called *enhanced* prongs.

As all gemstones are suitable for prong setting, it is the most frequently used method for jewelry. Prongs also offer greater flexibility when making adjustments for the size of an individual gemstone. Understandably, the more prongs, the more secure your gemstone will be. Generally, smaller gems use four prongs to allow more access for light.

Prong setting

Bezel setting

Prong setting is especially popular for solitaire engagement and bridal rings. Since the center stone is positioned higher, it is more prominent and easily seen. The height of the stone also provides greater access to light, allowing a gem to shine more brilliantly than other styles of setting.

Bezel setting

Bezel setting is an age-old technique, but one that is difficult to master. It imparts an elegant, tailored look, while providing a greater measure of security for the gem. Bezel setting employs a diskette of metal that holds the gem securely by its girdle. The diskette forming the bezel around the gem may be straight or scalloped, polished or textured. Rather than being held high by prongs, the gem is set into the body of the jewelry piece. This provides protection for its edges, girdle, and pavilion. Bezel setting is labor intensive and must be precisely crafted to match the outline of the gem.

A variation of the bezel setting is the *flush* setting, where the surface of the jewelry piece has a window cut into it that exactly fits the size of the gem. Secured from underneath, the crown of the gem rises from the piece, beautifully catching rays of light. When the setting half surrounds the gemstone, it is called a half-bezel or semi-bezel setting.

Bezel setting is well suited to people with active lifestyles. While it is an excellent choice for any style of jewelry, it is most useful for rings that frequently make contact with external objects.

Pavé setting

Pavé (pronounced *pa-vay*) *setting* is a very effective means of highlighting a large number of small stones. The name is derived from a French word meaning *to pave*. It is an appropriate description for the visual effect created by the pattern of gems, but does not refer to the method of setting. When used with diamonds or other colorless gems of high brilliance, pavé setting literally creates a sparkling "pavement" of light that is mesmerizing. The effect is created by setting each stone girdle to girdle, which allows little metal to be seen.

Pavé setting may be accomplished in many ways. One method uses a special tool (a graver) to pierce the surface of the jewelry piece and push over a small amount of metal. A second tool with a rounded, hollow end (beading tool) is pressed against the metal to form an attractive bead. Great care must be taken since a single slip of the graver can destroy an entire piece of jewelry.

Pavé setting   Channel setting

The second method involves handcrafting small beads using a thin wire and a jeweler's torch. Each bead is individually formed by a molten drop of metal. In some cases, a single bead may hold more than one stone in place. Either method takes a substantial amount of time, labor, and skill.

A third, and less labor-intensive method, involves casting a piece of jewelry with small beads surrounding each opening in the casting. This saves the jeweler the time it takes to hand fashion each of the three to four beads surrounding each gemstone.

Pavé setting often uses round stones, but many other shapes may be employed. In some cases, multiple stone shapes may be used in a single piece. The pavé style creates a bigger look since the gems are spread girdle to girdle over a large area on the jewelry's surface. Pavé setting is frequently used for diamonds in conjunction with white gold, creating the illusion that the whole piece is crafted from diamonds.

Channel setting

Channel setting is a technique whereby gemstones are set side by side with their girdles held between two long tracks of precious metal. When used with square, princess, and rectangular gems, the effect is breathtaking, as no metal appears between them. The gems appear as a river floating throughout the jewelry.

Gemstones in channel settings are set so closely together that no precious metal between them is necessary. This allows the set gems to display their maximum amount of brilliance. Understandably, it is very important that gemstones with precisely cut pavilions be used in channel setting. If not, the gemstones will crack during setting or be later lost. Often seen in eternity band rings and tennis bracelets, channel setting is increasingly common in modern jewelry designs featuring round, oval, princess, emerald, square, and baguette gems.

Bar setting

Bar settings are constructed from short bars that run like a railway track across the jewelry. Gemstones are individually set between these bars, leaving the sides of the gemstones exposed to light. An increasingly popular setting style, this technique maximizes the amount of light entering the gemstones, thereby optimizing brilliance and sparkle. The bar setting is a version of the channel setting and can often combine a contemporary and classic look in one design. It is best for rings featuring round, oval, princess, emerald, square, and baguette gems.

Bar setting

PRECIOUS METALS

Gold-type stamps

Most gold types have a stamp that designates the process and/or fineness. Generally, in the English system, an abbreviation has a period following the last letter. Gold fineness, for example, may be abbreviated K. or Kt. However, in practice, most jewelry stamps leave off the period (e.g., 14Kt or 14K). Some common abbreviations are listed below for quick reference:

10K(t).	10Kt Solid Gold
14K(t).	14Kt Solid Gold
18K(t).	18Kt Solid Gold
G.P.	Gold Plate
G.E.P.	Gold Electroplate
H.G.E.P.	Heavy Gold Electroplate
R.G.P	Rolled Gold Plate
G.F.	Gold Filled

Gold types

Jewelry products containing gold can be found in a variety of forms. Many pieces are manufactured entirely of karat gold, but others are not. Buyers should be aware of the various options that are available. These deliver comparable beauty but at a fraction of the cost of solid karat gold. It should be noted that the value of a piece is related to the amount of gold present and the degree of fineness. All types of gold products sold in the USA must be a **minimum of 10Kt fineness**. Here are the possibilities:

Gold flashed Also known as *gold washed*, this type of jewelry contains the smallest amount of gold relative to the size and weight of the item. The layer of gold on the exterior of a flashed piece is less than .175 microns in thickness.

Gold electroplate(d) To qualify for electroplate, the exterior surface of a jewelry piece must have a minimum layer of gold that is equal to or greater than .175 microns. This is equivalent to seven millionths of an inch (e.g., 14Kt G.E.P.).

Gold plate(d) Any piece of jewelry with a minimum layer of gold that is one-half micron (20 millionths of an inch) or greater may use this designation (e.g., 14Kt G.P.).

Heavy gold plate Similar to gold plating, the difference is in the minimum thickness of the layer. To obtain this designation, a piece of jewelry must have at least 2.5 microns (100 millionths of an inch) of karat gold to qualify (e.g., 18Kt H.G.E.P.).

Gold filled The term *gold filled* is sometimes used interchangeably with *gold overlay* or *rolled gold plate*. In this process, a substantial layer of karat gold is bonded to a support metal. Generally, gold-filled pieces are defined by the percentage weight of gold, with 1/20 (5%) being the minimum. Jewelry with a 14Kt layer meeting this standard can be stamped 14Kt G.F. or 14Kt R.G.P. In some cases, the full designation may be used (e.g., 1/20 14Kt G.F., or 1/20 14Kt R.G.P.).

If the percentage weight of a karat gold-filled piece is less than the minimum standard, it must be disclosed by the appropriate fraction (e.g., 1/40 14Kt R.G.P or 1/40 10Kt G.F.).

In practice, the consumer may see stamps such as 1/10 14Kt G.F. or 1/10 12Kt G.F. since the vendor is exceeding the minimum standard and wants to highlight that fact.

Solid gold This term is used to describe any jewelry item (or other product type) that is manufactured entirely of *10Kt* or finer gold alloy. If the product is pure *24kt*, then the term *solid gold* can be used without any modifiers. If a piece of jewelry is manufactured with a lesser gold fineness, then the fineness must also accompany the term solid gold (e.g.,

14Kt solid gold or 18Kt solid gold). In practice, jewelry is only stamped with the shorter designation, 14Kt or 18Kt. This identifies the piece as solid gold of the stated fineness. Solid-gold jewelry manufactured with a hollow center must be identified as such.

Vermeil Pronounced *vur-may*, the name of this process is derived from the French term for *veneer*. Vermeil jewelry is made entirely of sterling silver, but it contains an outer layer of fine gold. The only base metals present are those used to create the .925-fine silver alloy that qualifies as sterling. The layer of gold, whether electroplated or coated in some other fashion, must be of 10Kt fineness or greater and a minimum of 2.5 microns (100 millionths of an inch) in thickness.

An older term for this type of product was *silver gilt*. The original fire-gilding process was developed in France in the 18th century. A very famous collection of vermeil tableware, when not in use, can be seen on display in the Vermeil Room at the White House.

Gold leaf This is ultra-thin gold plating that's pounded and thinned, then applied to an object.

Silver

Silver has a rich history spanning more than 5,000 years, and like gold, it occupies a hallowed place in our collective history. It has been treasured by countless civilizations for its exceptionally high metallic luster, which, combined with its malleability and ductility, made it perfect for personal adornment. Associated with power, prestige, and a myriad of mythical powers over the centuries, it was crafted into objet d'art, religious artifacts, ceremonial weapons, silverware, tableware, and much, much more. Its use in currency can be traced back as far as the 7th century BC. So great was the allure and desire for silver that it was both the beginning and end of many kingdoms.

Silver is perfect for jewelry manufacture since it is soft, malleable, and takes an extremely high polish. In fact, silver is the most highly reflective of all metals. Its beauty, availability, and affordability make it the mainstay of fashion and design throughout the world.

Silver, like gold, can be found in more than one form, and as such, has standards to define its purity.

.925 sterling silver

Silver purity

Generally, a small amount of alloy is added to silver to help lessen tarnish and provide increased durability. Copper is the mainstay of silver alloys, but considerably smaller percentages of other metals are often present. Silver purity, like that of platinum, is expressed with a decimal number that indicates the amount of pure silver in parts per thousand. Silver standards vary around the world, but there are four that should be of interest to US consumers:

Fine silver	.999	99.9% pure silver
Britannia silver	.958	95.8% pure silver
Sterling silver	.925	92.5% pure silver
Coin silver	.900	90.0% pure silver

When the term *silver, solid silver,* or *sterling* is used to describe jewelry and other items, it refers to a product that is at least .925 pure.

Silver pricing

The small amount of copper added to sterling silver has little effect on the value. Instead, the price of silver items is affected by the labor and craftsmanship involved in finishing an item.

Platinum

Sixty times rarer than gold, platinum is only found in a few locations worldwide—Russia's Ural Mountains, South Africa's Merensky Reef, and a few small mines in the USA and Canada. Relatively new to the jewelry market, platinum is fast becoming incredibly popular and is already a bedrock of the contemporary jewelry landscape. Rarer, stronger, and denser than gold, it is considered by many to be the ultimate and most luxurious of all precious metals.

Platinum is much more difficult to work than gold due to its high melting point (approx.1773˚C versus 1064˚C for gold), but provides greater durability. Platinum may be abbreviated Pt. or Plat. when used in jewelry.

Platinum purity

Like silver, platinum purity is expressed by a decimal number that indicates the amount of pure platinum in parts per thousand.

The three most commonly seen platinum standards are:

.950:	95% pure platinum
.900:	90% pure platinum
.850:	85% pure platinum

Platinum group metals (PGM)

As the name implies, this group of precious metals includes platinum. Five other high-value metallic elements are also represented: iridium, rhodium, palladium, ruthenium, and osmium.

Some of these metals are alloyed with platinum or used to manufacture entire pieces of jewelry. Palladium, for example, has gained popularity as a jewelry metal in recent years.

Troy ounce

Precious metals such as gold and silver are often sold by the troy ounce. Many people do not realize that an ounce of gold is about 10% more than the typical ounce found at the grocery store. It is thought that the troy ounce was named after a weight system used in Troyes, France, during the Middle Ages. One troy ounce weighs 31.10 grams.

JEWELRY APPRAISALS

Since most jewelry has sentimental (as well as monetary) value, many individuals attempt to insure their jewelry in case of loss or damage. Estimates for replacement can vary considerably from appraiser to appraiser, dependent on their level of skill and experience. Finding the right professional can be challenging. Before seeking third-party appraisals, please consider the following:

Insuring jewelry

Do not assume that your jewelry collection is automatically insured by your household policy. Furthermore, it is always wise to take photos and catalog all of your jewelry. Try to keep all your receipts and retain as many written details as possible (e.g., lab reports, certificates of authenticity, appraisals). If your catalog is a hard copy, make sure you take a photocopy and keep the second copy at a friend's house—or as some collectors do, leave a copy with your family lawyer. If your catalog is a soft copy on your personal computer, make a copy of the data and keep it in a different location.

Valuation

An appraisal valuation is what someone is prepared to pay for something. For example, what is the value of the *Mona Lisa*? Is the value the same as the cost of the canvas and the paint, or is it determined by the amount that someone will pay for it? We believe that jewelry appraisals should reflect the average cost you would have to pay to replace the item if lost, stolen, or damaged beyond repair.

Independent

Jewelry Television offers appraisal services for a nominal fee. All appraisals are done by competent industry experts who have a solid record of accomplishment. These appraisers work independently of JTV and maintain a high degree of excellence by attending major trade shows on a regular basis and by participating in industry-related seminars and classes.

Since Jewelry Television is an integrated manufacturer and television home-shopping retailer, we have removed many of the middlemen that create additional layers of cost. For this reason, many jewelry appraisals exceed the expectations of our customers.

Unfortunately, we have also heard that some customers have had a negative experience when obtaining appraisals from local jewelers. While many jewelers thank us for increasing the awareness of colored gemstones, a few may feel threatened by television shopping networks and may try to discredit our jewelry. Please bear that in mind when seeking appraisals.

Knowledge

Most appraisers have extensive experience with precious metals and popular gemstones such as diamond, emerald, ruby, and sapphire. However, many may not have heard of the more exotic gemstones offered by Jewelry Television. When obtaining an appraisal, it is always a good idea to confirm that the appraiser possesses the requisite experience to value colored gemstone jewelry. This can be easily determined by asking if they have received any formal gemological training and to what degree.

As visual inspection is not a reliable method of identifying gemstones, please be sure to ask what tools will be used when performing your appraisal. A basic gem lab generally includes tools such as a refractometer, polariscope, dichroscope, microscope, Chelsea filters, UV lamp, and spectroscope. There may be specific gravity liquids or a hydrostatic balance to determine the relative density of various gems. Diamond testers and gram/carat scales are also common.

One question we are often asked is how appraisers can know the weight of gems without removing them from their settings. When dealing with stones mounted in jewelry, your appraiser must determine the dimensions of each stone, adjust for specific gravity (some gems are much denser than others are), and extrapolate a weight based on standard formulas by shape. Many factors, such as depth percentages, girdle width, and style of cutting, can modify the result. Please remember that the weight is only a "best estimate," based on careful examination and reasonable access to the stones within the setting. An exact weight can only be given if the stones are removed from your jewelry. In most cases, this is not practical or even possible without substantial risk of damage.

Tanzanite

Ruby ring

Yellow sapphire ring

Watermelon tourmaline

GEMS FROM A–Z

ABALONE SHELL

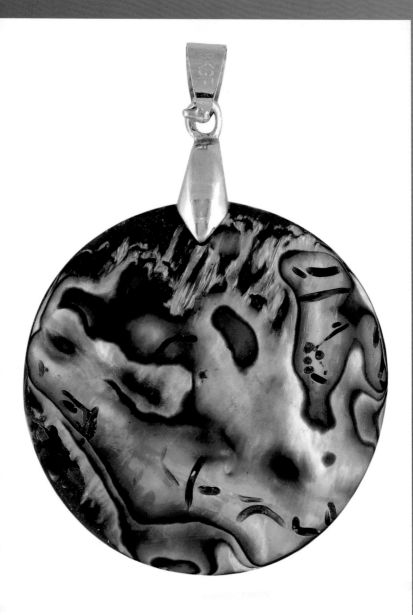

ABALONE SHELL

Abalone shell is the product of a univalve (single shell) marine mollusk that is highly valued by gourmets for its mild, delicate flesh. In addition to the shell, which exhibits a rich, iridescent play of colors, the abalone also produces an extremely rare and highly prized natural pearl. The shell, the meat, and the pearl of this mollusk have been treasured for millennia.

Legends and lore
Abalone shells have been worn for decorative, ritualistic, aristocratic, and spiritual purposes throughout history. Various cultures believed that the shell could calm or sooth emotions, foster imagination and creativity, and even benefit the heart, muscles, and digestion.

Just the facts
More than 100 species of abalone have been identified worldwide. The Spanish called this mollusc *oreja de mar*, which translates as *sea ear*, an allusion to the shape of the shell. It is believed the name *abalone* is derived from the Spanish word *abulón*. Other names for this mollusc include *paua* (New Zealand), *awabi* (Japan), and *ormer* (Great Britain).

Although abalone pearls are extremely rare, the vividly colorful, iridescent shells of this mollusk are in reasonable supply. Shells may be carved, but are often cut and polished for use in various forms of jewelry. Depending on the species of abalone, the iridescent colors may range from silvery to pink, green, blue, or purple.

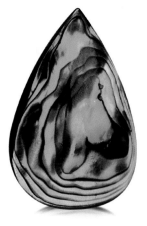

ABALONE:	Iridescent
Major Sources:	Worldwide coastal regions, North & South America, Australia & Europe
Colors Found:	Various, iridescent
Family:	Mother of pearl
Hardness:	2.5 to 4.5
Refractive Index:	1.530–1.685
Specific Gravity:	2.86
Crystal System:	Orthorhombic

Abalone shell

AGATE

AGATE

Agate **is the banded form of chalcedony (pronounced** *kal-ced-on-ee;* **cryptocrystalline quartz), and its name was derived from the site of its discovery, the river Achates (now Dirillo) in southwest Sicily. You will often find beautifully flowing patterns within agate, which are caused by the presence of iron and manganese.**

Legends and lore

Said by the ancients to render the wearer invisible, agate has been admired by humanity for thousands of years. Valued by the ancient Sumerians and Egyptians who used it for amulets and ornamental pieces, agate is one of the oldest known gems. In Roman times, agate *intaglio* (a gem carved in negative relief) signet rings were particularly popular.

Agate is mentioned in the Bible as being one of the "stones of fire" (Ezekiel 28:13-16) given to Moses and set in the breastplate of Aaron (Exodus 28:15-30). A variety of agate, *sardonyx* is one of the 12 gemstones set in the foundations of the city walls of Jerusalem (Revelations 21:19). As compiled by Andreas, Bishop of Caesurae, one of the earliest writers to tie the Apostles with the symbolism of the 12 gems of Jerusalem, sardonyx represents the Apostle James. Agate was especially valued during medieval times when one of the more outlandish uses was to bind an agate to each horn of an ox to ensure a good harvest. The danger here is that your agated beasts of burden may then become invisible and a little hard to find. Agate is believed to cure insomnia, ensure pleasant dreams, protect against danger, and promote strength and healing.

Just the facts

The main conditions necessary for agate formation are the presence of silica from devitrified volcanic ash, water from rainfall or ground sources, manganese, iron and other mineral oxides that form the white, red, blue, gray, brown, or black bands. Agates form by filling cavities in the host rock. As a result, they are often found as nodules with concentric bands like the rings of a tree trunk. (The bands sometimes look like eyes or even a landscape with trees.) Agate comes in many different forms, ranging from semitransparent to opaque. But a few of the agate varieties are blue agate, blue lace agate, crazy lace agate, green agate, Indian agate, moss agate, fire agate, tree agate, onyx, sardonyx, and wood agate.

AGATE:	Mentioned in the Bible
Major Sources:	Brazil, India, Mexico & South Africa
Colors Found:	Various
Family:	Chalcedony Quartz: SiO_2
Hardness:	6.5 to 7
Refractive Index:	1.53–1.54
Specific Gravity:	2.58–2.64
Crystal System:	Trigonal (aggregate)

Agate showing colorful bands

ALEXANDRITE

ALEXANDRITE

Known in Russia as the "gem of the tsars," *alexandrite* is truly a miraculous gemstone. Often described as an "emerald by day" and "ruby by night," when viewed under sunlight, alexandrite shows a teal to forest green. When seen by candlelight, though, it appears violet, crimson red, raspberry, purple, or orange.

Scant availability, remarkable color change, excellent durability, and a sparkling sub-adamantine or diamond-like luster make alexandrite a "must have" for any true jewelry connoisseur. A rare variety of chrysoberyl, alexandrite ranks alongside ruby and sapphire as one of the world's most coveted gemstones.

Legends and lore
Early one chilly October morning in 1830, a Russian peasant charcoal burner, Maxim Stefanovitch Koshevnikov, was making his way through the silver birch forests along the banks of the Tokovaya River. Tripping on the exposed roots of a large tree felled by a storm, he discovered some green gems. Quickly identified as emeralds, it was not long before this deposit in Russia's Ural Mountains was being mined for the famous green gem.

The Russian emerald mines also yielded other treasures, including a new gem that had the strange ability to change color. When viewed under sunlight, rich green colors appeared, but when seen by candlelight, it displayed reddish hues. The gem was named *alexandrite* after the young Tsarevitch, who was crowned Tsar Alexander II in 1855.

Legend has it that alexandrite was discovered by emerald miners on the Tsar Alexander's birthday, April 23, 1830, the year the Russian heir apparent came of age. But the date of the deposit's discovery and the alleged naming of the gem do not agree with one another. Vitaliy Repej, a Ukrainian alexandrite specialist, instead believes that alexandrite was actually discovered on April 3, 1834, by the Tsar's famous Finnish mineralogist, Dr. Nils Nordenskjold, and wasn't officially called alexandrite until 1842.

Its birthday aside, this new gem created a sensation—everyone wanted an alexandrite. But this was certainly no fun for the miners. Following the sparse alexandrite veins through pegmatite rock with hand-dug trenches, open pits, and small tunnels, mining was primitive to say the least. Imagine working through long winters plagued by biting cold and blinding snowdrifts. Summer brought no respite—just great swarms of gnats, mosquitoes, and gadflies.

The discovery of alexandrite on the future Tsar's birthday was considered especially fortunate, as the colors displayed by this unusual gem can mirror the Imperial Russian military colors of red and green. Possessing nationalistic connotations, alexandrite quickly gained popularity in Russia, where it was believed to bring good luck.

Because of its two colors, Russians believe it invites loneliness if you only wear one piece of alexandrite jewelry. The gem is also believed by crystal healers to strengthen the wearer's intuition in critical situations. Some also attribute alexandrite with the ability to aid creativity and inspire imagination.

Just the facts
In gemology, any chrysoberyl that changes color can be called alexandrite. The nomenclature is not dependent on the colors of the change. However, alexandrite's color change is dependent

on pure light sources (pure candescent light to pure incandescent light—for example, sunlight to candlelight).

Interestingly, the color-change effect is not unique to alexandrite. Many gem types can display a color change, such as sapphire and garnet. However, the degree of color change exhibited by alexandrite is among the most extreme encountered in natural gems.

Similar to emeralds, inclusions are a common feature in alexandrite. Inclusions record a gem's natural relationship with the earth. Given the prevalence of synthetic alexandrite, they are also a fascinating hallmark of authenticity that helps us distinguish genuine gems from those made by man.

ALEXANDRITE:	June's birthstone
Major Sources:	Brazil, India, Madagascar, Russia, Sri Lanka & Tanzania
Colors Found:	Teal, blue-green to forest green changing to violet, crimson red, raspberry, purple & orange
Family:	Chrysoberyl: $BeAl_2O_4$
Hardness:	8.5
Refractive Index:	1.74–1.76; Biaxial (+ or –)
Specific Gravity:	3.70–3.78
Crystal System:	Orthorhombic

Because of this gem's scarcity, alexandrite is found in a wide variety of shapes and sizes, faceted to maximize the carat weight and beauty of each individual crystal.

Coveted for its beautiful optical effects, the cat's-eye alexandrite combines a color change with the cat's-eye effect. Technically known as *chatoyancy*, this intriguing phenomenon is caused by parallel inclusions concentrating light into a single band. In order to show this effect, the gem must be cut as a cabochon.

While beautiful alexandrite is available from other locales, among alexandrite connoisseurs, Russian alexandrite maintains a historical pedigree that is highly coveted. In 1892, Edwin Streeter wrote in *Precious Stones & Gems*: "The wonderful alexandrite is an emerald by day and an amethyst at night. Its market value is extremely variable and sometimes as much as £20 per carat is paid for a fine stone." Today, the same Russian alexandrite is worth many thousands of dollars.

Although the Ural deposit closed after only a few decades, limited mining continues today. Little Russian alexandrite is available, and those lucky enough to own one truly are custodians of a gem from a bygone era.

From left to right: faceted and cat's-eye alexandrite (seen in daylight and incandescent light)

While it wasn't until 1996 that the tribal peoples of Andhra Pradesh unearthed the first hints of alexandrite in the Araku Valley, since its discovery, Indian alexandrite has endured a history as turbulent as Imperial Russia. From much needed mining regulation in 1999, to the destruction of coastal mines during the 2004 tsunami, Indian alexandrite has certainly had its ups and downs.

Always on the hunt for this stunning gem, we also encountered Indian alexandrite from a new locale, whose rich colors are reminiscent of alexandrite from the original Russian deposit. Today, Indian alexandrite primarily hails from Narsipattnanm, 62 miles inland from the first discovery in Vishnakahaputnam. It is characterized by an intense green with an incredible color change that ranges from vibrant amethyst to ruby red and reddish purple. Formed hundreds of millions of years ago during the Paleozoic era, it is believed that the pegmatite rocks found at the location of alexandrite's discovery in the Urals in Russia and at Narsipattnanm are the same. Mining Indian alexandrite is a dangerous business, and the tribal miners risk life and limb tunneling muddy soil to a depth of nearly 100 feet to find rocks rich with tiny clusters of alexandrite.

While gems from the famous Brazilian state of Minas Gerais have enchanted the world for over 100 years, a major new find was made in 1987 at Hematita. As with other mines containing pegmatite rocks, Brazilian alexandrite is found in rugged areas that can be difficult to access. Usually mined using primitive hand tools, one of the most famous exceptions is the Hematita mine, whose beautiful alexandrite is now quite scarce. Although the majority of Brazilian alexandrite is included, a tiny amount of better-quality gems has been unearthed. In 2004, a new pocket of Brazilian alexandrite was discovered, yielding blue-green alexandrite that changed to a delightful raspberry red. The best Hematita alexandrites can stand with any in the world.

Mines in Madagascar, Tanzania, and Mozambique have been producing good-quality alexandrite for several years. African alexandrite is typically located in wet regions near rivers and mined by sifting through river beds by hand to unearth the alexandrite-rich alluvials.

For approximately 90 years, Russia and Sri Lanka were the only known sources of alexandrite. Obtained from alluvial gravels (in contrast to most other deposits that are mined from the host rock), Sri Lankan alexandrite is characterized by a sapphire-green color in daylight with a change to columbine red, similar to purplish red spinel, in incandescent light.

Alexandrite ring in yellow gold

ALMANDINE

ALMANDINE

Almandine is the species of garnet most commonly associated with the January birthstone. While the name may be unfamiliar to the public, its brownish red to purplish red color is not. As the gemstone of choice for the first month of the year, almandine is well represented in many forms of jewelry.

Legends and lore

The name of this gemstone is purportedly derived from an ancient locality (Alabanda) in Turkey that was known for its production of reddish garnet. The name altered as it traveled through Latin (*alabandina, alamandina*) and finally arrived in English as *almandine*. As for the ancient Carian city that lent its name to the gem, all that remains of its former grandeur are a few ruins in the plains south of Aydin.

Just the facts

Almandine is one of six species of garnet in the realm of gemology. Chemically, it is an iron aluminum silicate mineral, but often lacks purity of composition. Almandine is one of three garnets that are commonly described as *pyralspites,* a sub-category within the garnet group. The name takes elements from each of its constituents (**pyr**ope-**al**mandine-**sp**essart**ite**).

All three garnets form a solid-solution series that often produces a mixture of two or even three species within a single garnet crystal. A garnet is considered almandine when the iron content is greater than the magnesium or manganese content of its pyralspite counterparts (pyrope and spessartite, respectively).

In nature, garnet exhibits two common habits (outward forms): the dodecahedron and the trapezohedron. Although a cubic mineral, it rarely exhibits the form of a cube. Almandine is found in metamorphic and pegmatitic rocks.

While red is the dominant color of almandine, it may appear brownish or exhibit a violet component. In cases where tone is too strong, gems may appear blackish. To lighten gems with darker tones, lapidaries often make the pavilions more shallow to lessen the effects of absorption.

ALMANDINE:	Named after the locality at Alabanda, Asia Minor
Major Sources:	Brazil, India, Madagascar, USA, Sri Lanka & Austria
Colors Found:	Brownish orange, red to purplish red
Family:	Garnet
Hardness:	6.5 to 7.5
Refractive Index:	1.780 to OTL
Specific Gravity:	4.05
Crystal System:	Cubic

AMAZONITE

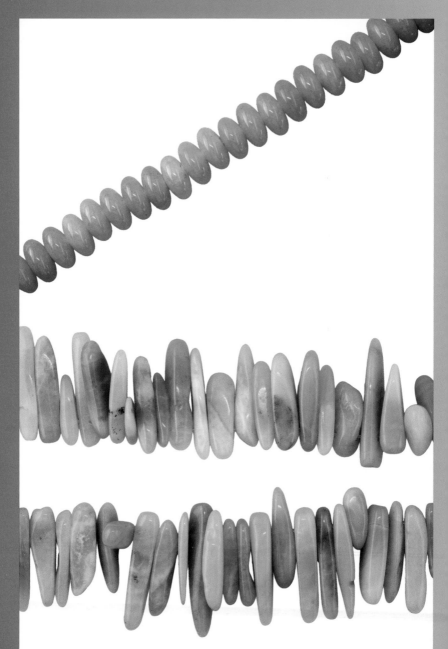

AMAZONITE

Amazonite **is an attractive, bluish green to green variety of microcline feldspar that often exhibits a schiller. This eye-catching phenomenon is caused by an interference effect created by layers of feldspar of slightly differing properties. When light makes contact with these layers, it is reflected and refracted at various levels within the host, producing a billowy light that seems to move throughout.**

Legends and lore

In folklore, amazonite is believed to enhance creativity, inspire confidence, improve physical stamina, and create a soothing effect on its bearer. It is sometimes called a *hope stone* and is considered a talisman of luck.

Just the facts

Amazonite (or *Amazon stone*) is an alkalai feldspar that is predominantly a potassium aluminum silicate; however, it often contains a small amount of albite, a plagioclase feldspar containing sodium. It is the presence of alternating layers of amazonite and albite that creates the schiller associated with this gemstone. Although the mechanism behind its color is not fully understood, some sources have suggested it is due to the presence of lead as well as iron in a divalent state.

AMAZONITE:	Very rarely crystalline
Major Sources:	Brazil, India, Madagascar, Kenya, Namibia, Russia & USA
Colors Found:	Green and blue-green
Family:	Feldspar
Hardness:	6.0 to 6.5
Refractive Index:	1.522–1.530
Specific Gravity:	2.56
Crystal System:	Triclinic

Amazonite borrows its name from a major geographic feature of Brazil, the Amazon. Brazil also serves as a major source of this mineral, as does Russia, Madagascar, and the USA. Although amazonite is generally greenish, it often has a mottled appearance. Since most rough is opaque to translucent, it is normally cut en cabochon. It has grown in popularity as supply improved, but it is still relatively unknown to the consumer. Attractive and affordable, amazonite makes a good choice for any style of jewelry.

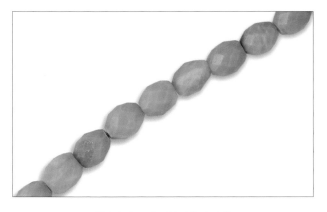

Checkerboard amazonite beads

AMBER

AMBER

Amber **is the ancient and fossilized resin of trees that grew in forests millions of years ago. Over the eons, chemical and physical changes occurred, fossilizing the resin to produce the amber we know today.**

Research indicates that amber ranges from about two million to 360 million years in age, although most gem-quality amber ranges from five million to 50 million years.

Amber is a unique gem. In addition to its beauty, it bequeaths humankind valuable scientific data through its ability to act as a window on the past. Its unique ability to preserve the organic tissues of prehistoric life forms is valued by both gem collectors and scientists.

Legends and lore

In classical times, amber was used medicinally and was also believed to offer a magical light for the deceased as they progressed through the underworld. Given this association, amber was once believed to provide magicians and sorcerers with special powers.

Other attributes associated with amber include love, strength, luck, healing, protection, and the ability to calm stressed nerves.

Just the facts

When you rub amber, static electricity is generated. In fact, the word *electricity* is derived from the ancient Greek word for amber, *elektron* or "sun made." Although amber is a fossilized plant resin that generally consists of organic carbon, hydrogen, and oxygen structures, the composition varies, depending on the type of parental plant species.

AMBER:	Preserves prehistoric life forms
Origins:	Burma, Dominican Republic, Germany, Poland & Russia
Colors Found:	Golden yellow, pale yellow, blue, green, deep cherry red to dark brown
Family:	Organic resin
Hardness:	2 to 2.5
Refractive Index:	1.53–1.55; SR
Specific Gravity:	1.05–1.09
Crystal System:	Amorphous

The process and transformation of tree resin into amber is not fully understood. However, there are several elements that are recognized as being essential, namely molecular polymerization (the combination of many molecules to form a more complex product of higher molecular weight), evaporation of turpenes (volatile oils—volatiles are substances that can be readily vaporized), heat, and pressure.

While the rate of transition from tree resin to amber is often represented as a linear process, in reality, it is variable. There are many different types of fossilized tree resins found all over the world. Each deposit has unique chemical components but can physically appear almost identical. In some cases, detailed chemical analysis is required to determine geographic origin.

Following its secretion, tree resin immediately begins to lose its original plasticity and harden. There are several forms of commercially exploited resin, including ambergris, Arabic gum, dammar, frankincense, gumlac (sometimes called *shellac*), kauri gum, mastic, myrrh, rosin, and sandarach.

Copal is a more mature form of resin. The word *copal* comes from the Spanish word *copalli*, which means "incense," an actual use of copal. Polymerization has now progressed significantly through the body of the resin. In some cases, the surface of the copal has fractured and crazed due to surface shrinkage prompted through the initial evaporation of turpenes, which can also commence during this period.

Distinguishing between copal and amber is a contentious issue among amber experts because there is no scaling system for assessing polymerization against age. Even though significant copal deposits exist in Colombia and South America that are less than 1,000 years old, the process of polymerization may take thousands of years before the resultant material can be called copal. This is because many external factors affect the rate of molecular linking.

The complete transition from resin to amber needs two additional factors present: heat and pressure. Heat and pressure may support the process of polymerization and turpene evaporation, but their full effect upon the formation of amber is not completely understood. The length of time needed to reach the point at which the majority of turpenes have escaped varies depending on surrounding conditions and the nature of the resin at the moment of its formation.

The organic inclusions commonly found in amber include plant debris, small animals, and a variety of prehistoric insects. These ancient creatures are predominantly extinct ancestors of today's cockroaches, ants, termites, caddis flies, centipedes, crickets, scorpions, and millipedes. These preserved life forms were trapped by fresh sticky resin that oozed from coniferous trees millions of years ago. Preserved in the amber, the insects are visible in almost perfect condition, showing the position they were in when they were entombed millions of years ago.

The most valued variety of amber for manufacturing jewelry and decorative objects is Baltic amber. Baltic amber is also known as *succinite,* after its parent *pinus succinfera,* a common tree in the Tertiary period, some 50 million years ago. The living tree that is thought to be the most visually similar is *agathis australis.* At present, the primary source of Baltic amber is the various deposits around the Russian port of Kaliningrad, the old German enclave of Koenigsberg. Annexed from the Germans after WWII, it is located on the southern Baltic coast between Poland and Lithuania. It is also called the Western Russian Enclave or Yantar Special Economic Zone (*yantar* is the Russian word for amber). Below 98 feet of sand around Kaliningrad, there is a 30-foot alluvial layer of amber containing clay called *blue earth.* It is mined from the surface in open pits with dredging buckets. The blue earth is then washed, and the amber is picked out by hand.

Typically yellow, golden, or brown, Baltic amber reportedly comes in 256 documented shades. The color of amber is influenced by changes in the resin when it is exuded from the tree.

Incredibly light, amber is occasionally buoyant in salt water, and Baltic amber is sometimes transported long distances by the sea, having been found as far away as the beaches of England and Scotland. It is from this ability that it gains one of its common names, *sea stone.* Important secondary sources include the Dominican Republic and Mexico.

Since the *Jurassic Park* movies, interest in amber with insect and animal inclusions has exploded, making it highly collectible. In regard to the film *Jurassic Park,* the alleged source of the dinosaur DNA was Dominican amber. Dominican amber is thought to be about 25 million years too young to truly contain dinosaur DNA. However, other amber sources from around the world could potentially contain the genetic material of these avian ancestors.

In 1994, a molecular biologist from California reported that he had extracted DNA from an insect sealed in amber 120 to 130 million years ago. Dr. Raul Canu claimed the insect was trapped when dinosaurs ruled the earth, leading people to speculate that Michael Crichton's novel could one day become a scientific reality.

AMBLYGONITE

Amblygonite **is a gemstone that is less well known than many of its peers. Its name is derived from two Greek roots meaning "blunt angles," an allusion to one of its more common crystal habits. Truly an exotic mineral, amblygonite is a "must have" for any gemstone collector.**

Legends and lore

There are many qualities attributed to amblygonite. Some believe that this gem creates a calming effect that provides balance in emotions and resolves conflict. Others feel that wearing amblygonite improves creativity and helps inspire new ideas.

Just the facts

Amblygonite belongs to a class of minerals known as *phosphates* and forms a solid-solution series with montebrasite. Its chemical formula is variable, allowing for many substitutions (e.g., (OH) for fluorine or sodium for lithium). Amblygonite is available in various shades of yellow to green and green to blue, but the color is rarely intense. Clean, transparent material of fine color is available, but supply is not consistent. Nearly all amblygonite in the market is color enhanced by irradiation, but naturally colored gems can be found. The polish luster of amblygonite ranges from vitreous to subvitreous. The main source of rough is Brazil, but smaller finds occur in Australia, Germany, Namibia, Sweden, and the United States.

Since amblygonite is considered a softer gemstone, it is better suited for pendants and earrings. However, with care, it can do well in rings and bracelets.

AMBLYGONITE:	Name means "blunt angle"
Major Sources:	Germany, Sweden, USA, Canada, Australia & Africa
Colors Found:	Various; most commonly yellowish, very rarely violet
Family:	Amblygonite
Hardness:	5.5 to 6.0
Refractive Index:	1.612–1.636
Specific Gravity:	3.01–3.11
Crystal System:	Triclinic

AMETHYST

Dionysus, known for his love of grape juice, was the Greek god of wine; however, after a few goblets, he became a little confrontational. One day in the forest, with goblet in hand, the tipsy Dionysus took insult from a passing mortal who refused to show him respect. The incident provoked his wrath, and Dionysus swore revenge on the next mortal that he saw...

Along came Amethyst, a beautiful young maiden on her way to pay tribute to the goddess Diana. Dionysus targeted Amethyst as the object of his revenge, and with the snap of his fingers, he summoned two ferocious tigers to devour the girl. As Dionysus sat back to enjoy the spectacle, Amethyst cried out to Diana. Seeing what was about to happen, Diana transformed Amethyst into a glimmering, pure-white quartz statue, thus protecting her from the ferocious tigers. Moved with guilt, Dionysus realized the ruthlessness of his actions and began to weep with sorrow. As the tears dripped into his goblet, Dionysus collapsed, spilling the tear-tainted wine onto the statue of Amethyst. The white quartz absorbed the wine's color, creating the colored gem that we refer to today as *amethyst*, the gemstone of the gods.

Legends and lore

With the mythology surrounding the origin of amethyst, it is perhaps fitting that it was once considered a talisman to prevent drunkenness, which explains why wine goblets were made from this gem. As the ancient Greeks often playfully manipulated words from other languages, it is possible that they jokingly converted the Hebrew word for a purple gem, *achlamath*, to the Greek word *amethustos*, meaning "not drunk," from which the modern name for amethyst is derived. In legend, it is usually taken literally, as if the Greeks really thought amethyst would prevent drunkenness.

Amethyst's shades of violet to purple have served as a symbol of royalty throughout history. Pharaohs, kings, and queens, as well as leading lights in religious sects, have long treasured it because of its rich, royal color.

Interestingly, this fascination with the color purple dates back to Roman times, when generals celebrating triumphs (and later, emperors who never fought a battle) got to wear a *toga picta* (a bright purple toga with gold embroidery).

Because amethyst was thought to encourage celibacy (it was believed to have a sobering effect not only on drunkards, but also upon those overexcited by passion), amethyst was very important in the decoration of Catholic churches in the Middle Ages. Considered to be the "papal stone," even today, bishops still wear amethyst rings.

Many other qualities were attributed to amethyst in the 15th century. Leonardo da Vinci wrote that amethyst was able to dissipate evil thoughts and quicken the intelligence. It was also believed to render people shrewd in business matters, preserve soldiers from harm, and assist hunters in capturing wild animals.

The history of adornment can be traced back to the Minoan period in Greece (circa 2500 BC), where amethyst has been found as polished cabochons set into gold rings. Popular in the 19th century, amethyst was a favorite gem in art nouveau jewelry.

Just the facts

Colored by an interaction of iron and aluminum, amethyst is a variety of macrocrystalline quartz that occurs in transparent pastel roses to deep purples and violets.

Like many other gemstones, the quality of amethyst varies according to its source. Amethyst from the Americas can be found in large sizes, as opposed to African amethyst (typically mined in Madagascar and Zambia), which is sometimes small but carries a higher saturation in color. Dark, highly saturated amethyst is also found in Australia and Sri Lanka. The now-historic Siberian variety is deep purple with occasional red and blue flashes and commands the highest price. However, the most prolific origin is Brazil, and if we were to believe Dionysus' wine was indeed the source of its color, Brazilian amethyst would have been born from the finest vintages.

AMETHYST:	February's birthstone
Major Sources:	Australia, Brazil, Kenya, Madagascar, Russia, Sri Lanka, Uruguay & Zambia
Colors Found:	Pinkish purple to violet
Family:	Quartz: SiO_2
Hardness:	7
Refractive Index:	1.54–1.55; Uniaxial (+)
Specific Gravity:	2.65
Crystal System:	Trigonal

First appearing in Europe in 1727, Brazilian amethyst soon became highly fashionable and expensive. Amethyst was very popular in France and England during the 18th century, and many affluent families invested large amounts of money in this gemstone. For example, a necklace of amethysts was purchased at a very high price for Queen Charlotte (1744–1818), wife of George III of England.

The chief mining areas for Brazilian amethyst are Minas Gerais, Bahia, and Marabá. Neighboring Uruguay also offers spectacularly beautiful varieties of amethyst.

Rose de france amethyst (also known as lavender amethyst) is the name for Brazilian amethyst of a pastel lilac hue. Rose de france amethyst was a very popular Victorian gem, and while it frequently appears in antique jewelry, it is currently experiencing a revival in popularity as part of a general awakening to the beauty of pastel gems.

Bi-color amethyst beautifully melds the regal purple lavenders of amethyst with the ice whites of white quartz in one gem. Bi-color amethyst occurs because of environmental changes during formation. At different times, the color-causing element (iron) was incorporated into the crystal, causing different color layers. Purposely cut to showcase this feature, bi-color amethyst is generally judged by the balanced contrast between its colors. Cutting the gem so both colors show is sometimes challenging for cutters. While notoriously difficult to cut consistently, a well-cut bi-color gem is a real delight.

From left to right: Uruguayan amethyst, rose de france amethyst, and bi-color amethyst

AMETRINE

Ametrine **is one of the world's most unusual gemstones in that it is actually two gems in one. Bi-color ametrine blends the golden sunburst of citrine with the violet sunset of amethyst.**

Legends and lore

A romantic story to be sure, legend has it that the first ametrine was discovered by a Spanish conquistador in the 17th century. Upon reaching the remote Pantanal wetlands of eastern Bolivia, it is said that he encountered a peaceful tribe of hunter-gatherers known as the Ayoreo. As chance would have it, the chieftain had a daughter whose beauty and allure immediately attracted the attention of the conquistador. Love flourished, and a wedding soon followed. As a dowry, the chieftain gave the conquistador a mine that was treasured by the Ayoreo for its beautiful bi-color crystals. Today, we know those crystals as *ametrine*, and the dowry as the Anahí mine. It is an enchanting legend but one whose facts are steeped in mystery.

Ametrine is said to posses all the metaphysical benefits of both amethyst and citrine, as well as its own unique properties. Some believe that it aids in meditation, relieves tension, disperses negativity, and helps eliminate prejudice.

Just the facts

The unusual color variation found in ametrine is due to the presence of iron in different oxidation states within the crystalline structure. The different oxidation states are responsible for absorbing different wavelengths of light, which create two color centers—one responsible for citrine and the other, for amethyst. Exactly how this occurs is not fully understood.

The main source of fine-quality ametrine is the Anahí mine of eastern Bolivia. Prior to 1980, ametrine was an obscure mineral known only to collectors and gemologists. However, from 1980 and forward, production increased, and ametrine began to appear in larger quantities, allowing for production in jewelry. It was not long

AMETRINE:	Bi-color gem
Major Sources:	Bolivia
Colors Found:	Golden & violet
Family:	Quartz: SiO_2
Hardness:	7
Refractive Index:	1.54–1.55; Uniaxial (+)
Specific Gravity:	2.65
Crystal System:	Trigonal

before popularity and demand brought this beautiful, exotic gem into the mainstream of both the jewelry and gemstone industries. An alternate name, *bolivianita*, is often heard in the mining district.

Ametrine

One challenge when cutting ametrine is the proportion of color within each crystal. When centered with a 50/50 or 60/40 split, much of the original crystal is wasted. Common shapes include rectangles and rectangular octagons, generally with a simple step cut to highlight the bi-color split.

In recent years, miners and dealers have sought ways to maximize the yield from ametrine crystals by attempting new shapes with innovative styles of faceting. These new cuts tend to blend colors, creating a graduation of shades within the host. These artistic blends of amethyst and citrine colors create a new look and allow for greater opportunities in design.

AMMOLITE

AMMOLITE

Ammolite **is a truly exotic treasure of nature. It is made from the mineralized fossil of a long-extinct marine invertebrate known as an** *ammonite.* **Like opal, ammolite shows a stunning play of color that is visually mesmerizing. Discovered in shale deposits of Southern Alberta, Canada, these vibrantly iridescent shells are over 70 million years old.**

Legends and lore

Reference to ammonites can be found in a diverse range of cultures throughout history. In England, these shells were thought to be the coiled remains of headless snakes turned to stone, hence the name *snakestone.* In Germany, ammonite fossils were known as *dragon stones* and were believed to be a defense against evil spells. In Asia, Feng Shui masters associate ammolite with wealth, prosperity, and good fortune. Special attributes are even associated with the various iridescent colors displayed by the shell.

Just the facts

Ammolite is the gemstone that comes from the mineralized fossil of ancient ammonites. Although ammolite was discovered in the early 1900s, it was, for all practical purposes, unavailable until the 1980s. It was at the beginning of this decade that a commercially viable source of iridescent shell was found.

AMMOLITE:	As solid, doublet, or triplet
Major Sources:	Canada & USA
Colors Found:	Various, iridescent
Family:	Ammonite
Hardness:	2.8 or by top of triplet material
Refractive Index:	1.520–1.680 (varies/triplet/doublet)
Specific Gravity:	2.70 (varies/triplet/doublet)
Crystal System:	Orthorhombic

Ammonite shells are composed primarily of aragonite, but may contain other minerals. Color can cover the full spectrum of the rainbow, but reds and greens are more prevalent. Generally, the layer of color is very thin, so after polishing, it requires some form of backing to increase durability. Another consideration is hardness. Ammolite generally ranges from 3.5 to 4 on the Mohs' scale, which means it is susceptible to scratching. Therefore, most ammolite gemstones are assembled pieces in the form of doublets or triplets. Solid pieces are quite rare and expensive, but are highly prized by collectors.

The opal-like play of color in ammolite is due to the structure of microscopic aragonite crystals, which interfere with the passage of light. The thickness of the layers and the uniformity of stacking are major factors in the resultant color.

The process of cutting and polishing ammolite takes great care and precision. Since the layer of color is frequently very thin (less than 1mm in thickness), it is easy to polish through the layer and end up with a dull, lifeless piece of ammolite. Maximizing the intensity and play of color while providing a fine polish takes a great deal of skill.

Ammolite triplet set

ANDALUSITE

Andalusite, **an aluminum silicate, derives its name from the site of its discovery, Almeria, in the southern Spanish province of Andalucía.**

While andalusite's color play has been compared to alexandrite, this is technically incorrect, as pleochroic (displaying different colors in different directions) gemstones like andalusite feature all their colors at once. Alexandrite only changes color in different light sources.

Legends and lore

Some andalusite crystals have carbonaceous inclusions, arranged so that in cross section they form a dark cross. This variety is called *chiastolite* (named after the Greek word for "cross") and sometimes referred to in ancient texts as "lapis crucifer," meaning "cross stone." Chiastolite is found in schist formations near the town of Santiago de Compostela, northwest Spain, and many amulets of the cross stone were once sold to pilgrims. It is often mentioned as a gemstone of protection and was once used to thwart evil eye curses.

Andalusite is considered by crystal healers to be a gemstone that enhances intellect, problem-solving abilities, and mental clarity. It is also mentioned as being conducive to the receipt of messages from the netherworld.

Just the facts

Andalusite is polymorphous with two other gem minerals, kyanite and sillimanite. This means they are identical in chemical composition but differ in crystal structure. Andalusite typically occurs in thermally metamorphosed pelitic rocks and in pelites that have been regionally metamorphosed under low-pressure conditions. It also occurs, together with corundum, tourmaline, topaz, and other minerals, in some pegmatites.

This gem's main claim to fame is its extraordinary pleochroism. When cutting strongly pleochroic gemstones (iolite, tanzanite, kunzite, etc.), lapidaries typically try to minimize the pleochroism and maximize the single-most attractive color. Interestingly, andalusite is the opposite, as all the colors visible in different directions are attractive. Cutters, therefore, try to orient the gem to get a pleasing mix of its orange, brown, yellow, green, and golden colors. When cut successfully, andalusite looks unlike any other gemstone, displaying patterns of color dancing around its facets.

ANDALUSITE:	Noted for its pleochroism
Major Sources:	Brazil, Mozambique, Spain & Sri Lanka
Colors Found:	Brown, green, orange, red & white
Family:	Andalusite: Al_2SiO_5 + Fe
Hardness:	7.5
Refractive Index:	1.62–1.65; Biaxial (−)
Specific Gravity:	3.05–3.20
Crystal System:	Orthorhombic

Andalusite

ANYOLITE

Anyolite **was discovered in 1954 near Longido, in northeastern Tanzania. It is a metamorphic rock used as an ornamental gem material.**

Just the facts

The most conspicuous components of anyolite are green zoisite and red corundum, often accompanied by a small amount of black hornblende. The latter tends to give the rock a speckled or streaked look.

ANYOLITE:	Ruby in zoisite
Major Sources:	Tanzania
Colors Found:	Green & black with red/pink ruby inclusions
Family:	Ruby in zoisite
Hardness:	6.5–7 (zoisite), 9.0 (ruby)
Refractive Index:	1.70 spot (zoisite) to 1.76–1.77 spot (ruby)
Specific Gravity:	3.10–3.40 varies depending on ratio of ruby to zoisite
Crystal System:	Orthorhombic–dipyramidal

Since it is opaque, anyolite is often cabbed or fashioned into beads for use in jewelry. It is also carved into a wide range of decorative items. Carvings generally take advantage of the difference in hardness (6.5 for zoisite versus 9 for corundum), often focusing on the ruby component. The name is derived from a Maasai word *anyoli*, meaning "green." An alternate name in the trade is *ruby in zoisite*. Tanzania still remains the primary source.

Ruby in zoisite

APATITE

APATITE

While it sounds like it's hungry, it's actually trying to fool you. The name *apatite* comes from the Greek word *apatao*, meaning "to deceive," as apatite has often been confused with gems such as tourmaline, peridot (olivine), and beryl. Ironically, the phosphates in bones and teeth of all vertebrate animals are members of the apatite group, so the hunger connection is quite appropriate after all.

Legends and lore

Apatite is said to enhance one's insight, learning abilities, and creativity and to give increased self-confidence. It also is said to help achieve deeper states of meditation. Using apatite is said to facilitate the desired results when working with other crystals. Apatite is also believed by crystal healers to be useful in improving one's coordination, strengthening muscles, suppressing hunger, and easing hypertension.

Just the facts

Apatite is actually three different minerals, depending on the predominance of either fluorine, chlorine, or the hydroxyl group: calcium (fluoro, chloro, hydroxyl) phosphate. These ions can freely substitute in the crystal lattice, and all three are usually present in every crystal, although some specimens are almost 100% pure in one group. Gem-quality apatite is rare, particularly over one carat. The color is often due to the presence of rare earth elements and includes green, yellow, blue, violet, and a yellow-green variety originally mined in Spain (commonly called *asparagus stone* because of its similarity in color to the vegetable). Cat's-eye apatites also exist.

APATITE:	Series of related minerals
Major Sources:	Brazil, Burma, Madagascar, Mexico, Mozambique & Sri Lanka
Colors Found:	Blue, green, violet, yellow & yellowish green
Family:	Apatite: $Ca_5(PO_4)_3(OH,F,Cl)$
Hardness:	5
Refractive Index:	1.62–1.65; Uniaxial (–)
Specific Gravity:	3.16–3.23
Crystal System:	Hexagonal

While apatite wasn't unearthed in Madagascar until 1995, the French began working the Fort Dauphin area in the 1930s, after shepherds found some gems. Located in the southeast of Madagascar, practically at the end of the world, Fort Dauphin was established in 1642 and abandoned in 1674, following an 18-month siege by Antanosy tribesmen. It is believed that the famed pirate republic of Libertalia was later established there. The recent finds of apatite in Madagascar have added to the popularity of this gem. Exhibiting excellent saturation, Madagascan apatite's colors range from neon emerald greens (as typified by our Fort Dauphin apatite) to neon paraíba blues

Apatite

Cat's-eye apatite

AQUAMARINE

AQUAMARINE

Symbolizing the near-perfect clarity and transparency of the ocean, the sheer beauty of *aquamarine*, with its wonderful color and fantastic clarity, makes it popular with both the collector and the wearer of fine jewelry. It will come as no surprise that its name was derived from the Latin words for "water of the sea."

Blue, one of the world's most popular colors, is famous for its calming effect, and out of all the blues available, none matches the serenity found in aquamarine. Aquamarine embodies all that is natural. Aquamarine, the sparkling birthstone for March, ranges from pastel blue to light green, its tones reminiscent of an invigorating sea breeze.

Legends and lore

Since antiquity, aquamarine has been seen as a gemstone of great vision, its crystals often being used as eyes in the creation of statues that symbolize power and wisdom. According to legend, any man or woman that set eyes on these statues became a person of great wisdom, harnessing the ability to see into the future.

On occasions, these statues were placed in strategic positions near the coastline, where they could calm the wrath of the god Poseidon, thus ensuring the safe return of those on ships at sea.

Aquamarine has long been associated with its ability to capture oceanic energy. When amulets made of aquamarine were worn, sailors believed that unmatched bravery would be instilled in their souls. These fishermen's friends accompanied their owners while out on the high seas, and in the event of a storm, were tossed overboard to placate Poseidon's anger. Interestingly, Thai culture contains a common belief that aquamarine can ward off seasickness and prevent wearers from drowning. Because of its association with the sea, aquamarine is considered to be a gemstone of purification and cleansing that washes the mind with fresh, clear thoughts and promotes self-expression. Its calming effects make it a popular gemstone for those who practice meditation, as it is also believed to eradicate fears and phobias.

AQUAMARINE:	March's birthstone
Major Sources:	Afghanistan, Brazil, Madagascar, Mozambique, Namibia, Nigeria, Pakistan, Tanzania & Zambia
Colors Found:	Pastel blue to bluish green
Family:	Beryl: $Be_3Al_2Si_6O_{18}$
Hardness:	7.5 to 8
Refractive Index:	1.56–1.60; Uniaxial (–)
Specific Gravity:	2.68–2.74
Crystal System:	Hexagonal

Just the facts

Colored by trace amounts of iron, aquamarine is a member of the beryl family, whose members also include emerald, red emerald (bixbite), goshenite (colorless), heliodor (yellow), and morganite (pink). The color ranges, depending on the relative concentrations and location of iron within the beryl crystal structure. While noted for its excellent clarity, inclusions are more prevalent (and accepted) in the more intense hues.

Brazil has been the world's major supplier of aquamarine for decades. The famous Marambaia area is one of the most important sources of fine aquamarine in the world. Today, however, several African nations, including Nigeria, Mozambique, Zambia, and Madagascar, provide an equal, if not greater, supply of similarly beautiful examples. The different shades of aquamarine are distinguished by their own names. *Santa Maria* is the name of the rare, intensely deep blue aquamarine found in the Santa Maria de Itabira mines of Brazil. Since 1991, very similar colors have also been found in certain mines in Africa, especially in Mozambique, where they have come to be known as *Santa Maria Africana*.

Another Brazilian beauty is the deep blue *Espirito Santo*, coming from the state of the same name. And *Martha Rocha* aquamarine takes its name from a 1954 Brazilian beauty queen.

Recognized as a gem-producing country since Portuguese colonial times, Mozambique is increasingly becoming more visible in the global gem community, primarily due to its excellent-quality aquamarines. Mozambique governmental poverty eradication policies have been key factors in the development of the mining industry, creating conditions for prospecting projects to take place at a national level.

Cushion aquamarine

Trillion aquamarine

AVENTURINE

Aventurine's name is derived from an accident. During the 18th century, Venetian glass workers were preparing molten glass when copper filings accidentally fell into the batch, producing glass with sparkles. The name *aventurine* comes from the Italian *a ventura,* which means "by chance." But make no mistake—aventurine is certainly not glass. It is actually a much sought-after member of the chalcedony quartz family.

Legends and lore

Aventurine has been used as a lucky talisman and is a popular gem for gamblers.

Legends say that it is an all-purpose healer, used to reduce stress, develop confidence and imagination, and improve prosperity. An ancient legend from Tibet tells of its use to help nearsightedness and to improve the wearer's creativity.

Many crystal healers believe that aventurine has the capacity to calm a troubled spirit, balance emotions, and bring an inner peace. It is also believed to enhance leadership qualities, allowing the wearer to act decisively with strong intuitive power.

Just the facts

Aventurine is a type of quartzite (a quartz-bearing rock) that contains small inclusions of one of several shiny minerals which give the gem a glistening effect. The glistening effect of aventurine is known as *aventurescence*. The color of the aventurescence depends on the mineral included in the gem. Mica inclusions give the gem a yellow or silver glitter or sheen. Goethite and hematite inclusions give the gem a red or gray glitter or sheen. Chrome-green fuchsite mica inclusions give the gem a green sheen. This is the most common variety.

AVENTURINE:	Aventurescence
Major Sources:	Brazil, India & USA
Colors Found:	Blue, brown, creamy green, green & peach
Family:	Quartz: SiO_2
Hardness:	7
Refractive Index:	1.54–1.55
Specific Gravity:	2.64–2.69
Crystal System:	Trigonal (aggregate)

Aventurine ranges in color from green, peach, brown, blue, and creamy green. If a color is not stated with the word *aventurine,* it is usually assumed to be green. In the past, green aventurine has been labelled *Indian jade.*

Aventurine

AZURITE

Azurite **has been valued for many centuries, but not only as a gemstone. Its rich blue color was highly prized as a dye for use in fabrics and paints. The name, which alludes to its color, is derived from a much older Arabic word,** *al lazuward,* **meaning "blue." The English equivalent is "azure."**

Legends and lore

Egyptians, Greeks, Romans, and other ancient cultures considered azurite of great importance. Crushed and powdered, it could be turned into a rare, blue pigment that was prized above many other valuable commodities. By the 1700s, it was considered the color of monarchs and aristocracy, gaining the prestigious moniker *royal blue* throughout Europe. In the metaphysical realm, it is believed to have healing and curative powers.

AZURITE:	Commonly found with malachite
Major Sources:	Worldwide, Australia, Chile, Mexico, Morocco, Namibia, USA & Zaire
Colors Found:	Dark blue & violetish blue
Family:	Azurite
Hardness:	3.5 to 4.0
Refractive Index:	1.730–1.836
Specific Gravity:	3.80
Crystal System:	Monoclinic

Just the facts

Azurite is a copper carbonate mineral that is found in the oxidation zones of copper deposits and is considered a secondary ore of copper. Azurite is highly prized by specimen collectors due to its wide range crystal habits. Gemstone collectors are much more limited in their choices since most transparent facetable crystals are small. Generally, gems over one carat in size appear overly dark, bordering on black.

Azurite is commonly found in conjunction with malachite, a green copper carbonate mineral into which it slowly alters. A mix of the two minerals is often called *azurmalachite*. Azurite is soft (3.5 on the Mohs' scale) and opaque. When set in jewelry, it is in the form of cabs or beads. Color ranges from light to dark blue, with medium to dark blue being more common.

Azurite

BENITOITE

Benitoite **is a rare collector's gem that was discovered in 1907 in San Benito County, California, USA. (This locality served as its only commercially viable source until the mine closed in 2005.) In 1985, the California legislature declared benitoite the state gemstone. Its name is derived from the locality.**

Legends and lore

The discovery of benitoite was pure luck. In 1907, a prospector looking for other natural resources stumbled upon a cave that contained a large number of blue crystals. Not sure what had been found, samples were ultimately sent to the University of California at Berkeley. After nearly a year of intense study, it was determined that a new, unidentified mineral had been discovered.

Just the facts

The most interesting feature of benitoite is its structure. As the science of crystallography developed, it was theorized that there were 32 different mineral classes. These classes served as a basis for defining the six crystal systems used to categorize minerals. Prior to the discovery of benitoite, there was no example for the ditrigonal dipyramidal class within the hexagonal system. In 1907, benitoite gained the distinction of being the first mineral to display this type of symmetry.

Benitoite is special in many ways. Its dispersion is so strong that its fire rivals that of diamond in lighter material. Another notable feature is its strong fluorescence. Under short-wave ultraviolet light, it exhibits a strong, bluish white glow.

Chemically, benitoite is a barium titanium silicate. Luster is vitreous, and hardness is moderate at 6-6.5 on the Mohs' scale. Pleochroism is strong (blue and colorless).

Benitoite can be colorless, but often ranges from light to dark blue, sometimes with a slightly purple component. Pink crystals have been found on rare occasions. Benitoite has been manufactured in jewelry, but due to its limited supply, it is extremely difficult to find. Well-formed triply-terminated crystals, when available, are highly prized by specimen collectors.

BENITOITE:	State gemstone of California
Major Sources:	San Benito County, California
Colors Found:	Blue, violetish blue, colorless & white; very rarely pink; can be bi-colored; has higher dispersion than diamond
Family:	Benitoite
Hardness:	6.0 to 6.5
Refractive Index:	1.757–1.804
Specific Gravity:	3.68
Crystal System:	Hexagonal

Benitoite

BERYL

The name *beryl* is from the ancient Greek *beryllos,* for the precious blue-green color of sea water. This was originally applied to all green gemstones, but later used only for beryl. Some scholars believe the word beryl is related to the ancient trading city of Belur or perhaps has ancient Indian origins (being derived from the old Hindi word *velurya* or the Sanskrit word *vaidurya*).

As an allochromatic gem, when absolutely pure, beryl is devoid of color. Small amounts of metallic elements can be present in the crystal structure, giving rise to many color variations. Aquamarine, emerald, red emerald, Fire Beryl™ (goshenite), morganite, and heliodor are all members of the beryl family.

Just the facts

The most common beryl varieties are listed below. Beryl is famous for its perfect, hexagonal prismatic crystals that occur individually or in clusters. These range in size from the microscopic to enormous giants of 25 feet or more. Understandably, only very small amounts of these enormous crystals are of a sufficient quality to be used in jewelry.

All beryl varieties can be faceted into various gem cuts, and some beryls display phenomena such as asterism (star effect), chatoyancy (cat's-eye effect), and an unusual effect in emerald called the *trapiche*. Trapiche emeralds are found only in Colombia.

BERYL:	Perfect, prismatic hexagon crystals
Major Sources:	Afghanistan, Brazil, Colombia, Pakistan, Russia, South Africa, Tanzania & Ukraine
Colors Found:	Various
Family:	Beryl: $Be_3Al_2Si_6O_{18}$
Hardness:	7.5 to 8
Refractive Index:	1.56–1.60; Uniaxial (–)
Specific Gravity:	2.66–2.87
Crystal System:	Hexagonal

THE BERYL FAMILY:	
Aquamarine:	Pastel greenish blue to blue
Emerald:	Intense green
Bixbite:	Red
Goshenite:	Colorless
Heliodor:	Yellow to yellowish green
Morganite:	Pastel pink to salmon

Morganite

Emerald

Heliodor

BIXBITE

Bixbite was named in honor of Maynard Bixby, the individual credited with its discovery in 1904. Found in the Thomas Range of Utah, the first specimens of this rare red beryl were small and of poor quality. However, a second find in 1958 proved more fruitful. Gem-quality crystals were found in the Wah Wah Mountains of Beaver County, Utah.

Legends and lore

The discovery of gem-quality red beryl was an accident, or some might say pure luck. While searching for deposits of uranium, fortune smiled on a prospector by the name of Lamar Hodges. His discovery provided the first supply of facet-grade rough.

Just the facts

The color of bixbite ranges from red to violet-red and is attributed to the presence of manganese in a +3 oxidation state. Gemstones are normally small and often exhibit inclusions, which are acceptable due to the extreme rarity. Clean, transparent gemstones over one carat are difficult to find and highly prized by collectors. Crystals of bixbite are generally prismatic or long and barrel-shaped. Most crystals are too small to be faceted and serve as specimens for mineral collectors.

The name *bixbite* is now eschewed in favor of *red beryl*, due to the existence of another mineral by the name of *bixbyite* (also named after Maynard Bixby). In some cases, the term *red emerald* is also used.

BIXBITE:	The red variety of beryl
Major Sources:	Utah & New Mexico
Colors Found:	Purplish red to orange-red; stone colors will be more saturated than seen in morganite and of a darker tone
Family:	Beryl
Hardness:	7.5 to 8.0
Refractive Index:	1.566–1.572
Specific Gravity:	2.66–2.70
Crystal System:	Hexagonal

Princess-cut bixbite

Fancy-cut bixbite

CALCITE

The mineral *calcite* has been included in many grammar school science books. It is commonly used to demonstrate the property of double refraction. Although very soft for a gemstone, calcite is sometimes faceted for collectors. Its diverse range of colors and exotic-looking habits make it a popular choice for anyone starting a specimen collection.

Just the facts

At 3 on the Mohs' scale of hardness, calcite is soft in comparison to most gemstones. However, with proper care and respect, gemstones can be appreciated in any collection. Color in calcite is diverse and spans the entire spectrum of the rainbow. When used in jewelry, it is often bezel set to protect the stone from external contact. Seen predominantly in silver, many designers take advantage of its various forms of banding to create aesthetic appeal. Calcite is often used in bead jewelry.

Calcite holds a special place of importance in the realm of mineralogy. It was instrumental in helping scientists formulate many theories on the structure and optical properties of crystals. In 1812, Friedrich Mohs selected calcite to represent one of ten minerals on his newly devised scale of hardness.

CALCITE:	Best example of double refraction
Major Sources:	Worldwide notable locales– New Jersey, Mexico & Iceland
Colors Found:	Colorless or white; many other color varieties due to trace elements and/or inclusions
Family:	Calcite
Hardness:	3.0
Refractive Index:	1.486–1.658
Specific Gravity:	2.70
Crystal System:	Trigonal

Optical calcite, an extremely clean, colorless variety, has many scientific applications. It is commonly used as a component in refractometers, polarimeters, dichroscopes, and polarizing microscopes. Some of the best material for this purpose comes from Iceland and Mexico.

Calcite is calcium carbonate, which, interestingly, can be produced organically or inorganically. Aragonite, which has the same chemical formula, is a dimorph of calcite. The polish luster of calcite ranges from vitreous to subvitreous.

Calcite can be found throughout the world, but there are a number of notable sources in addition to Iceland and Mexico. Canada, England, France, Germany, Norway, Russia, and the United States provide an excellent supply of fine-quality material.

Calcite

Brown calcite

CARNELIAN

Carnelian is an ancient gem that has been prized throughout history for its reddish color. Its alternate name, *cornelian,* adds to the confusion over its etymology. Various sources attribute its derivation to three different Latin roots: *cornum* (cherry), *cornus* (horn), and *carnis* (meat). Two of the roots, *cornum* and *cornus,* seem to be better options since they are associated with the cornelian cherry tree that is prevalent throughout Europe and the Mediterranean region.

Legends and lore

Carnelian has been an important gem in nearly every great civilization. From the royalty of Ur (the Mesopotamian capital of pre-biblical times) to Napoleon (he returned from his Egyptian campaign with a huge octagonal carnelian) and Tibetan Buddhists, carnelian has been revered for its healing, spiritual, and creative qualities.

A gem of great religious significance, carnelian was used by the Egyptian goddess Isis to protect the dead on their journey through the afterlife.

Carnelian is mentioned in the Bible as being one of the "stones of fire" (Ezekiel 28:13–16) given to Moses for the breastplate of Aaron (Exodus 28:15–30) and is also one of the 12 gemstones set in the foundations of the city walls of Jerusalem (Revelations 21:19). It is the symbol of the Apostle Philip.

Popular in ancient Greece and Rome for intaglio (a gem carved in negative relief) signet rings, the Romans symbolically associated dark-colored carnelian with men and light-colored carnelian with women.

Muhammad's seal was an engraved carnelian set in a silver ring.

To this day, Buddhists in China, India, and Tibet believe in the protective powers of carnelian and often follow the Egyptian practice of setting the gem with turquoise and lapis lazuli for enhanced power.

CARNELIAN:	Mentioned in the Bible
Major Sources:	Brazil, India, Madagascar, Sri Lanka & Uruguay
Colors Found:	Orange to red
Family:	Chalcedony quartz: SiO_2
Hardness:	6.5 to 7
Refractive Index:	1.53–1.54
Specific Gravity:	2.58–2.64
Crystal System:	Trigonal (aggregate)

Just the facts

Carnelian is a variety of quartz that comes to us in the form of cryptocrystalline aggregates. The crystals are so small, in fact, that it would take substantial magnification to distinguish their individual forms. Carnelian ranges from translucent to opaque and is often fashioned into cabs, tablets, or beads for use in jewelry. There is no clearly defined division between carnelian and sard; however, sard is generally browner. The color of carnelian is due to trace amounts of iron oxide.

Carnelian

CHALCEDONY

CHALCEDONY

In the realm of gems, the name *chalcedony* does double duty. It is commonly used to describe a bluish variety of cryptocrystalline quartz, but also has a more general application. It is used as a sub-category within the quartz species that is inclusive of all cryptocrystalline quartz varieties. The name is possibly derived from *Chalcedon*, an ancient port of Bithynia, near present-day Istanbul, Turkey.

It has a waxy luster and appears in a great variety of colors, including blue, white, buff, tan, green, red, gray, black, yellow, and brown. Different colored varieties of chalcedony have individual names, including agate (banded), bloodstone (green with red spots), chalcedony (blue to brownish blue), chrysoprase (apple green), carnelian (orange to red), flint (dull gray to black), jasper (spotted red, yellow, brown, or green), and sard (light to dark brown).

Legends and lore

The Romans prized chalcedony as seals, and in the New Testament (Revelations 21:19), It is one of the 12 gemstones set in the foundations of the city walls of Jerusalem. As compiled by Andreas, Bishop of Caesurae, one of the earliest writers to tie the Apostles with the symbolism of the 12 gems of Jerusalem, chalcedony represented the Apostle St. Andrew.

Chalcedony was used during the Renaissance as a magic amulet to promote health and safety. It is also one of the gemstones used in commesso, or Florentine mosaic. Developed in Florence in the late 16th century, commesso is a technique of fashioning pictures with thin, cut-to-shape pieces of brightly colored gems.

Just the facts

Quartz gemstones are commonly separated into two groups based on the size of their individual crystals. The macrocrystalline large crystal quartz group includes many popular gemstones, such as amethyst, ametrine, citrine, and green amethyst (prasiolite). Cryptocrystalline quartz includes quartz aggretates whose individual crystals are too small to be easily distinguished. Varieties of cryptocrystalline quartz include sard, carnelian, agate, heliotrope, and chrysophase. Many of these gems have been coveted since antiquity.

Normally faceted as a cabochon, it is often used to great effect in both necklaces and bracelets.

CHALCEDONY:	Waxy luster
Major Sources:	Brazil, India, Madagascar, Mexico, South Africa, Tanzania & USA
Colors Found:	Black, blue, brown, buff, green, gray, red, tan, white & yellow
Family:	Quartz: SiO_2
Hardness:	6.5 to 7
Refractive Index:	1.53–1.54
Specific Gravity:	2.58–2.64
Crystal System:	Trigonal (aggregate)

Purple chalcedony

Faceted chalcedony

CHAROITE

CHAROITE

***Charoite* offers an intriguing array of patterns that range from eye-catching to mesmerizing. The patterns often exhibit a combination of swirls, veins, and spots that give each piece a unique and magical appearance.**

Just the facts

The name *charoite* is used to describe both a mineral and an attractive gem material whose primary constituent is charoite. The gem material, which was discovered in a remote, mountainous region of Russia, is classified as a rock. Some sources attribute its name to a locality, while others insist that it comes from a Russian root, meaning "magical" or "charming." The latter seems more appropriate, considering the exotic patterns that make charoite so special.

Color ranges from lilac to purple or violet, with many shades present within a single piece. In addition to charoite, other minerals such as microcline feldspar and tinaksite are commonly present in substantially smaller percentages.

These minerals add to the variety of colors and patterns that make this gem material so stunning.

Charoite is commonly carved into a wide range of decorative and ornamental objects, which are highly prized by collectors and art lovers. When used in jewelry manufacture, it is most often seen in the form of a cab. The only known source of charoite is found in the Sakha Republic of Eastern Siberia, near the Chara River.

CHAROITE:	May exhibit chatoyancy
Major Sources:	Russia
Colors Found:	Purple with black, gray, or white swirls
Family:	Charoite
Hardness:	5.0 to 6.0
Refractive Index:	1.550–1.559 (varies by composition)
Specific Gravity:	2.68
Crystal System:	Monoclinic

Charoite beads

CHRYSOBERYL

It is the gem of springtime, youth, and innocence. And its name, *chrysoberyl*, is derived from the Greek words for golden, *chryso*, and green gemstone, *beryl*.

Its rarest variety, alexandrite (the color-change variety), is quite well known, although the number of people who have heard of it is probably 100 times greater than the number who have ever seen it and 1,000 times greater than the number who have ever owned it.

Legends and lore
Said to bring peace of mind and increase self-confidence, chrysoberyl also promotes kindness, generosity, benevolence, hope, optimism, renewal, new beginnings, compassion, and forgiveness.

Just the facts
When cut, chrysoberyl is an extremely brilliant gem, one that is rapidly gaining in popularity.

Displaying attractive golden lemons, limes, greens, oranges, and chocolates, together with an extreme brilliance, chrysoberyl is exceptionally tough, making it ideal for everyday wear. The color in yellow chrysoberyl is due to traces of iron.

Cat's-eye chrysoberyl is a translucent gem ranging in color from a honey yellow or honey chocolate to yellowish green to apple green.

It is known for its reflected light effect called *chatoyancy* (cat's eye). This is achieved by

CHRYSOBERYL:	Chatoyancy
Major Sources:	Brazil, India, Madagascar Russia, Sri Lanka, Tanzania, Zambia & Zimbabwe
Colors Found:	Brown, yellow & yellowish green
Family:	Chrysoberyl: $BeAl_2O_4$
Hardness:	8.5
Refractive Index:	1.74–1.76; Biaxial (+ or −)
Specific Gravity:	3.70–3.78
Crystal System:	Orthorhombic

cutting a gem that has small, parallel *silk* inclusions into a cabochon. As the gem is rotated, it exhibits a distinct, silvery-white line across its dome that seems to open and close like a cat's eye.

It is so coveted that if you just mention cat's-eye, it is assumed to be in reference to cat's-eye chrysoberyl.

Exceptional-quality chrysoberyl has recently been unearthed in Magara, Tanzania, a region made famous by tanzanite and tsavorite.

Chrysoberyl

CHRYSOPRASE

Chrysoprase's **name comes from the Greek words** *chrysos,* **meaning "gold," and** *prason,* **meaning "leek," due to its color similarities with the vegetable.**

One of the most coveted varieties of chalcedony quartz, chrysoprase is prized for its apple-green color and rarity.

Legends and lore

Chrysoprase was used by the Greeks, Romans, and Egyptians in jewelry and other ornamental objects. In ancient Egyptian jewelry, chrysoprase was often set together with lapis lazuli.

It is mentioned in the Bible as being one of the 12 gemstones set in the foundations of the city walls of Jerusalem (Revelations 21:19) and is the symbol of the Apostle St. Thaddeus.

Chrysoprase was also popular in the 14th century when the Holy Roman Emperor Charles IV used it to decorate chapels, including the Chapel of Saint Wenceslas in Prague.

A favorite gem of Frederick the Great of Prussia and Queen Anne of England, chrysoprase is believed by crystal healers to increase grace and inner equilibrium.

Just the facts

Chrysoprase can vary in color from yellowish green to apple green and grass green, depending on the levels of hydrated silicates and nickel oxides present in the gem.

Because of its semi-opaque green color, chrysoprase was often mistaken for imperial jade (jadeite).

Other types of green chalcedony include prase (a very rare, less vivid green chalcedony found in eastern Europe, Delaware, and Pennsylvania) and mtorolite (a variety of green chalcedony colored by chromium and found in Zimbabwe).

CHRYSOPRASE:	Mentioned in the Bible
Major Sources:	Australia, Brazil, Madagascar, Russia, South Africa, Tanzania & USA
Colors Found:	Apple green
Family:	Chalcedony Quartz: SiO_2
Hardness:	6.5 to 7
Refractive Index:	1.53–1.54
Specific Gravity:	2.58–2.64
Crystal System:	Trigonal (aggregate)

Chrysoprase

CITRINE

CITRINE

Citrine is the yellow variety of macrocrystalline quartz that takes its name from citron, the French word for lemon. Citrine is a beautiful, transparent gemstone and one of November's birthstones.

Legends and lore

Citrine was first used in jewelry in Greece during the Hellenistic period (end of the 4th to the end of the 1st century BC).

Its first use by the Romans was in intaglios (gems carved in negative relief) and cabochons in the first centuries after the birth of Christ.

In antiquity, citrine was believed to be the gemstone of happiness and used as a protective talisman against evil thoughts.

Among its many historic medicinal uses, it was believed to aid digestion, remove toxins from the body (citrine was once commonly used as a charm against snakebites and venomous reptiles), provide protection against the plague and bad skin, and to be useful in the treatment of depression, constipation, and diabetes.

Among crystal healers, citrine is said to be especially useful in stimulating one's mental capacities, enhancing creativity and intuition, and bolstering one's self-confidence. It is thought to give emotional control, while making one more alert. Citrine is also said to be very helpful in assisting one to acquire and maintain wealth.

Just the facts

Citrine occurs naturally in proximity to amethyst and is a related quartz mineral. Its color is due to small amounts (approximately 40 parts per million) of iron in the crystal structure of quartz.

The color ranges from pastel lemon yellow to golden yellow to mandarin orange and madeira red (after the color of the wine). Traditionally, the madeira shades were more coveted, but these days, many people prefer citrine's brighter lemon tones. Most of the citrine mined today comes from Uruguay, Brazil, and many African nations, including Madagascar. It can be easily confused with topaz and has even been called *topaz quartz*.

Bi-color citrine beautifully melds the bright golden yellows of citrine with the ice whites of white quartz in one gem. And it occurs because of environmental changes during formation. At different times, the color-causing element (iron) was incorporated into the crystal, causing different color layers. Purposely cut to showcase this feature, bi-color citrine is generally judged by the balanced contrast between its colors. Cutting the gem so both colors show is sometimes challenging. While notoriously difficult to cut consistently, a well-cut multicolored gem is a real delight.

CITRINE:	November's birthstone
Major Sources:	Brazil, Madagascar, Mozambique, Tanzania, Uruguay & Zambia
Colors Found:	Shades of yellow
Family:	Quartz: SiO_2
Hardness:	7
Refractive Index:	1.54–1.55; Uniaxial (+)
Specific Gravity:	2.65
Crystal System:	Trigonal

Checkerboard-cut citrine

COPAL

Copal can be thought of as baby amber. Like its much older counterpart, it is a hardened resin. Copal was well known in the New World and played a pivotal role in the culture of many Mesoamerican Indian tribes. Although commonly used as incense, it had further importance in religious and ritualistic practices.

Just the facts

Copal is similar in appearance and chemistry to amber. Opinions vary from source to source as to what distinguishes one organic gem from the other, and no clearly defined standard exists. One fact does remain—copal is substantially younger than amber.

Generally, copal is softer than amber and crazes more easily. It also contains more volatile compounds due to the lack of polymerization, which is a function of age and time. Copal is, however, an affordable and attractive alternative to amber. It is often used in the manufacture of jewelry and can be found in various colors, some natural and some enhanced. It is not unusual to see insects, bugs, and various plant matter within copal. In rare cases, even small animals may become trapped before the resin hardens.

COPAL:	Organic gemstone often with insect inclusions
Major Sources:	South America
Colors Found:	Orange, yellow & brown
Family:	Copal resin
Hardness:	2.0 to 2.5
Refractive Index:	1.540
Specific Gravity:	1.06
Crystal System:	Amorphous

Polished copal with insect

Green copal

CORAL

Coral **is one of the better-known organic gemstones. Its beauty has been cherished and prized throughout antiquity. Although there are hundreds of species of coral worldwide, only a very small number are used in jewelry manufacture.**

Just the facts

Coral is the product of a coral polyp, a primitive marine animal that looks similar to a plant. Its body is tube-like in shape and contains eight small tentacles at the top. Its main source of food is small plankton carried by water currents.

When many people think of coral, they picture beautiful, exotic atolls in remote portions of the vast Pacific Ocean. These coral reefs do not supply the highly prized gemstone seen in the jewelry industry. That honor is left to *Corallium rubrum* and *Corallium japonicum*.

Coral growth varies by type, ranging from approximately one to 25 centimeters per year. Some branching corals may attain the latter growth, but are affected by changes in water temperature, pollution, and turbidity. Coral used for jewelry manufacture thrives at 13°C to 16°C, a factor that limits its range. For *Corallium rubrum* and *Corallium japonicum*, size is generally limited to branches less than two feet in length, the diameter of which rarely exceeds two inches at the widest point.

Coral colors generally range from pink to deep blood red, white to orange, and brown to black. Most coral is harvested along the coastal waters surrounding Australia, Japan, Malaysia, the Philippines, and Taiwan. It is also found in the Mediterranean Sea, and to a lesser extent, the Red Sea.

CORAL:	Current production limited by environmental regulations
Major Sources:	Coastal Mediterranean, Asia & USA
Colors Found:	Red, pink, white, black & blue
Family:	Calcareous coral
Hardness:	3.0 to 4.0
Refractive Index:	1.486–1.658
Specific Gravity:	2.65
Crystal System:	Trigonal

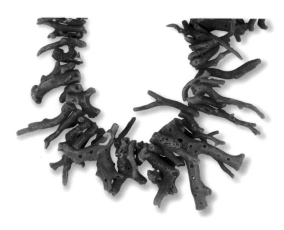

Italian red coral strand

DANBURITE

Danburite **is an exotic mineral that is not well known to the consume**
Discovered near Danbury, Connecticut, it is named after the localit
Danburite is prized by specimen collectors and gemstone enthusiasts.

Just the facts

Danburite is a calcium boron silicate that is relatively hard at 7-7.5 on the Mohs' scale. It is primarily available in pastel shades of yellow or pink, but it is often colorless. Traditional styles of faceting give it good brilliance, but concave cutting gives the gem additional life and beauty.

Although danburite was first discovered in Connecticut, most of the gems today come from Mexico (Other sources of danburite include Japan, Madagascar, Russia, and the United States.) Clean, transparent rough is available for cutting, but clean, larger gems are becoming more difficult to obtain.

Trillion Quantum-cut® danburite

DANBURITE:	Named after first place of discovery: Danbury, CT
Major Sources:	Mexico, Madagascar & Burma
Colors Found:	White, orange, yellow & brown
Family:	Danburite
Hardness:	7.0 to 7.5
Refractive Index:	1.630–1.636
Specific Gravity:	3.00
Crystal System:	Orthorhombic

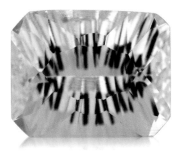

Mexican Quantum-cut® danburite

DIAMOND

The word *diamond* comes from the Greek word *adamas*, meaning "unconquerable" or "invincible."

"Diamonds are forever," sang Shirley Bassey, while Marilyn Monroe insisted they were "a girl's best friend." Celebrated in song, over the last century, diamond (April's birthstone) has become the most marketed of gemstones.

Legends and lore

The myths and facts associated with the diamond transcend cultures and continents.

The world's first known reference to this gemstone comes from an Indian Sanskrit manuscript, the *Arthsastra* (which translates as "The Lesson of Profit"), written by Kautiliya, a minister to Chandragupta of the Mauryan Dynasty (322–185 BC).

Plato wrote about diamonds as living beings, embodying celestial spirits. Roman literature makes its first distinct mention of them only in the 1st century AD, in reference to the alluvial diamonds found in India.

The ancient Greeks and Romans believed they were tears of the gods and splinters from falling stars. Cupid's arrows were supposed to be tipped with diamonds, thus having a magic that nothing else could equal.

The Hindus believed that diamonds were created when bolts of lightning struck rocks. They even placed them in the eyes of some of their statues.

Jewish high priests turned to diamonds to decide the innocence or guilt of the accused. A diamond held before a guilty person was supposed to dull and darken, while a diamond held before an innocent person glowed with increasing brilliance.

The Romans wore diamonds because they were thought to possess broad, magical powers over life's troubles, being able to give the wearer strength, invincibility, bravery, and courage during battle.

Kings of antiquity led battles wearing heavy leather breastplates studded with diamonds and other precious gems because it was believed that diamonds possessed god-given magical qualities and powers far beyond the understanding of humankind. Thus, warriors stayed clear of kings and those who were fortunate enough to have the magical diamonds in their breastplates.

An act of Louis IX of France (1214–1270) established a sumptuary law reserving diamonds for the King, indicating the rarity and value of this gem.

Until the 14th century, only kings could wear diamonds because the gems stood for strength, courage, and invincibility. Small numbers of diamonds began appearing in the 14th century in European regalia and jewelry, set mainly as accents among pearls. But the possession of extraordinarily large and noble diamonds was always the privilege of royal houses and rich families. As an example, the imperial crown of the Russian Tsarina Catherine the Second (1729–1796) was mounted with 4,936 sparkling diamonds.

In the Middle Ages and the Renaissance, every ring set with a precious gem was not considered as much a piece of jewelry as an amulet that bestowed magical powers upon its wearer. Diamonds, when set in gold and worn on the left side, were believed to hold the power to drive away nightmares, ward off devils and phantoms, and soothe savage beasts. A house or garden touched at each corner with a diamond was supposed to be protected from lightning, storms, and blight. The gems were also supposed to impart virtue, generosity, and even to calm the mentally ill. Not only was it commonly believed that diamonds could bring luck and success, it was also thought that they could counter the effects of astrological events.

Just the facts

As a gemstone lover, you may have heard about the 4 C's related to valuing gemstones and, in particular, diamonds. While other factors, such as origin, sometimes need to be taken into consideration when valuing colored gemstones, below is a basic guide to the 4 C's that diamond professionals and connoisseurs the world over rely on: cut, color, clarity, and carat weight.

DIAMOND:	April's birthstone
Major Sources:	Africa, Australia, Brazil, Canada, India & Russia
Colors Found:	Various
Family:	Native element: carbon
Hardness:	10
Refractive Index:	2.41–2.42; SR
Specific Gravity:	3.53
Crystal System:	Cubic

Color

Colorless and near-colorless diamonds are rare, beautiful, and highly prized among connoisseurs. To the untrained eye, most diamonds look white. However, to the professional, there are small differences in the degrees of whiteness seen.

Cut

With round brilliant cuts accounting for over 80% of diamond sales worldwide, ask anyone what a diamond's shape is, and they will probably say round. Despite this shape, there are many other beautiful diamond cuts that warrant serious consideration. The eight most popular diamond cuts are: emerald cut, heart cut, marquise cut, oval cut, round brilliant cut, pear cut, princess cut, and radiant cut.

Unlike colored gemstones, diamonds are cut, shaped, and proportioned to a remarkably uniform ideal. In 1919, the Russian mathematical genius Marcel Tolkowsky, a member of a large and powerful diamond family, published his opinions of which diamond proportions result in the optimum balance of brilliance and fire.

White diamond

18Kt white gold diamond ring

Carat weight

Unlike colored gemstones, diamonds are generally cut to a uniform ideal for maximum brilliance (white light reflections), fire (flashes of color), and scintillation (play of light). With this uniform cutting and their proportions, we can very conveniently and accurately equate diamond carat size with their millimeter size.

Clarity

Inclusions are tiny, natural features within the body of a diamond. Nearly all gemstones contain some inclusions; however, many are microscopic and can only be seen under magnification. While the prevalence and acceptability of inclusions vary from gemstone to gemstone, in general, if they do not interfere with the beauty of a gem, they are not only accepted, they are also a fascinating hallmark of authenticity that records a gem's natural relationship with the earth.

Round Brilliant-Cut Diamond	
Size	Typical Weight
1 millimeter	0.01 carat
2 millimeter	0.03 carat
3 millimeter	0.10 carat
4 millimeter	0.25 carat
5 millimeter	0.50 carat
6.0 millimeter	0.75 carat
6.5 millimeter	1.00 carat
7.0 millimeter	1.25 carat
7.5 millimeter	1.65 carat

Diamond grading

Developed by the Gemological Institute of America (GIA), this system is now common-place for the retailing of diamonds across the globe and consists of a diamond clarity scale and a diamond color scale.

Diamond color scale

Prior to the introduction of the GIA grading system, the letters A, B, and C were used to grade diamonds. Because the GIA wanted a fresh start, though, they decided to begin with the letter D.

Pairs and suites

Pairs, or suites, of diamonds matched for color, clarity, and cut are more highly valued per carat or per gem than single diamonds of the same quality. Given the rarity of many diamonds, a matching set is disproportionately

Black diamond

14Kt white gold black & white diamond ring

hard to find and, thus, commands a higher per carat price than if each of the diamonds from the suite was sold separately.

Color-enhanced diamonds

Most colored diamonds found in jewelry today are treated. The process, known as color enhancement, involves using clean diamonds and modifying their color with a combination of electron bombardment and heat, using safe electron-accelerator technology. This enhancement duplicates the processes that produce colored diamonds within the earth. All color-enhanced diamonds sold by JTV are treated in the USA to certified international standards.

Unlike with some other diamond treatments, color-enhanced diamonds are treated to fulfill preferences for vivid color only; this coloring technique does not try to hide or dissipate flaws. The myriad of popular diamond colors produced using this technology includes blue, green, red, orange, yellow, pink, purple, and black. The real beauty and popularity of these diamonds lie in the fact that they combine both the rich color hues of colored gems like rubies and sapphires with the unforgettable brilliance and sparkle of a diamond. In other words, they virtually become "two gems in one."

Color-enhanced diamonds fall into three general categories: irradiation, high-pressure/high-temperature (HPHT) heating, and coatings. While the color alterations of irradiated and HPHT-enhanced diamonds are throughout the stone, the colors of coated diamonds are on the surface only (usually only on the pavilion). This means that, like all coated stones, such as mystic topaz, coated diamonds require special care. Avoid exposure to heat, chemicals, and acids. Do not clean them with steam or ultrasonic cleaners; coated gems are not suitable for re-cutting or re-polishing. If the coating is damaged, the stone can be recoated without problem. Coated diamonds are generally seen in the pink, red, and purple colors that are difficult to produce by irradiation or HPHT treatment.

Multi-colored diamond ring in yellow gold

Blue, red, yellow, green, and champagne colored diamonds

Diamond Color Grading Scale

D, E, F	These purest tints are rare and comparatively expensive. Their rare color assigns them a higher market price.
G, H, I	Often offering much better value, to the untrained eye, they seem the exact same color as the more expensive D, E, and F colors.
J, K, L	Discounted for their barely perceptible yellowish tints, diamonds in this range offer excellent value.
M to Z	These are further discounted for their more distinct yellow hues.
Z+	Diamonds whose color intensity is outside the normal range are called *fancy colors* and come in about any color you can imagine (e.g., pink, red, green, purple, black, blue, yellow, and more).

Diamond Clarity Grading Scale

FL = FLAWLESS	No inclusions or blemishes of any sort under 10x magnification when observed by an experienced grader.
IF = INTERNALLY FLAWLESS	Has no inclusions when examined by an experienced grader using 10x magnification, but will have some minor surface blemishes.
VVS1 to VVS2 = VERY VERY SLIGHTLY INCLUDED	Contains minute inclusions that are difficult even for experienced graders to see under 10x magnification.
VS1 to VS2 = VERY SLIGHTLY INCLUDED	Contains minute inclusions that are difficult even for experienced graders to see under 10x magnification.
SI1 to SI3 = SLIGHTLY INCLUDED	Contains minute inclusions (such as small crystals, clouds, or feathers) when observed with effort under 10x magnification. The SI3 diamond clarity grade was created because many in the diamond industry felt that there was too wide a gap between SI2 and SI1. After the EGL (European Gemological Laboratory) started issuing certificates with the SI3 grade, the *Rapaport Diamond Report* (the definitive price guide for diamonds) added SI3 to its price list.
I1 to I3 = INCLUDED	Contains inclusions (possibly large feathers or large included crystals) that are obvious under 10x magnification.
PK = PIQUE	Contains inclusions easily visible to the naked eye.

DIOPSIDE

DIOPSIDE

Diopside **was named in 1800 from the Greek word** *dis,* **meaning "double" and** *opsis,* **meaning "vision," in reference to the pleochroism (different colors displayed when viewed from different angles) found in its prismatic form.**

Legends and lore

Diopside is also called the "crying gemstone" because it is believed by crystal healers to heal trauma by bringing forth cleansing tears. It is assumed to bring creativity to the wearer and is said to be related to love and commitment. Crystal healers believe that, when worn close to the chest (such as in a pendant), diopside can benefit the heart, lungs, and circulation.

Just the facts

Diopside is a calcium magnesium silicate found in metamorphosed impure limestone, meteorites, and igneous basalts. It was previously named *schefferite, white schefferite,* and *zinc-schefferite.*

The mineral diopside is the magnesium-rich member of the clinopyroxene group.

Diopside crystals have a perfect cleavage in two directions, are often twinned, and are short and columnar, but with an uneven fracture. Mineralogists easily recognize diopside in the field by its crystal habit, color, fracture, cleavage, and white or white-green streak.

Diopside is typically white, blue, purple, brown, green, colorless, and gray, with a glassy luster. The less common shades are yellowish brown and greenish brown.

Varieties of diopside include *chrome diopside* (a chromium-rich diopside known for its deep green color), *violan* (a rare blue variety found in Italy), *cat's-eye diopside* (green with the effect due to inclusions of parallel needles), *malacolite* (a white-colored variety), *salaite* (an iron variety), *dekalbite* (an iron-free variety), and *star diopside* (a star with four rays).

Gem-quality diopside is mined in Siberia, Burma, India, Italy, Sri Lanka, Brazil, Madagascar, South Africa, and Pakistan. Uzbekistan, located between Tajikistan and Turkmenistan, is becoming an important locality for a variety of Russian diopside called *tashmarine.* This variety has a slightly lower chromium content than the Siberian material, a less saturated color, and can display gray or brown tones. India has the largest deposits of cat's-eye or star diopside. The color of African diopside tends to be a more yellowish color similar to peridot.

DIOPSIDE:	Perfect cleavage in two directions
Major Sources:	Brazil, Burma, India, Madagascar, Pakistan, Russia, South Africa, Sri Lanka & Uzbekistan
Colors Found:	Blue, brown, colorless, green, gray, purple & white
Family:	Pyroxene: $CaMgSi_2O_6$
Hardness:	5 to 6
Refractive Index:	1.66–1.73; Biaxial (+)
Specific Gravity:	3.22–3.38
Crystal System:	Monoclinic

Chrome diopside

As the name implies, chrome diopside owes its color to traces of chromium. It has a beautiful, rich-green color, similar to that of fine emeralds or the rarest tsavorite garnets. While there is little historical information regarding this rare gem, some claim it is beneficial for health, relationships, spirituality, and financial success.

One major reason chrome diopside is relatively unknown is that it has only recently become available in sizable commercial quantities. It displays strong birefringence and has a vitreous luster. It is mostly available in small sizes, with large carat weights hard to find.

Chrome diopside is mostly mined in Yakutia, Siberia (Russia). Yakutia territory is located in the extreme north of Asia and is considered the coldest place in the northern hemisphere. Mining is limited due to cold winters lasting for nine months; hence, this gem is seasonal, and it has been difficult to maintain a steady supply. Interestingly, Yakutia is also the source of 99% of all Russian diamonds. Chrome diopside is a diamond mine indicator mineral and is sometimes found as an inclusion inside diamonds. The liberalization of the economy of the former Soviet Union has made chrome diopside more available than ever before.

Star diopside

Star diopside is also known as *black star diopside* because of its blackish color. Asterism, or the star effect, is a reflection that appears as two or more intersecting bands of light across the surface of a gem. Star diopside has four rays, two of which are straight, while the other two are not at right angles to the first pair. This gem is mainly mined in India and is generally a black or blackish green color.

Cat's-eye diopside

Chatoyancy, or the cat's-eye effect, is a reflection that appears as a single bright band of light across the surface of a gemstone. Cat's-eye diopside, which is green, is mainly mined in India, but it is also found in Burma.

Violan

Violan is light blue to purple in color due to the presence of large amounts of manganese. Mined mainly in Italy, violan is generally used for beads and inlay—faceted gems are always tiny.

Russian chrome diopside

Shanseres™

If you enjoy soft, pastel shades of green, then *Shanseres*™ is the choice for you. This exotic gem comes from Asia, but does not derive its color from the presence of chromium, like its darker green relative. Discovered in the mountains of China, Shanseres™ was found along an area that borders the ancient silk trade route. Its name, *shan*, meaning "mountain," and *seres*, a derivative of the Chinese word for silk, is an allusion to this past.

Until the discovery in China, this pistachio-colored gemstone was in extremely short supply. Even with the find in China, the supply is still not robust. Shanseres™ is a "must have" for the collector and a welcome addition to any piece of jewelry. It is only available at Jewelry Television.

SHANSERESE™:	Non-chrome green diopside
Major Sources:	Burma, Finland, India, Madagascar, South Africa, USA & China
Colors Found:	Light green to green
Family:	Diopside
Hardness:	5 to 6
Refractive Index:	1.675–1.701
Specific Gravity:	3.29
Crystal System:	Monoclinic

Oval Chinese Shanseres™

Rectangular octagonal
Chinese Shanseres™

EMERALD

For more than 4,000 years, the deep "green fire" of *emerald* has been treasured as a symbol of eternal spring and immortality.

Shrouded in myth and lore, the birthstone for May isn't just a beautiful gem. Emeralds are also ornaments of power and politics that have created legends and molded world history.

Prized by Egyptians, Romans, Aztecs, crowned heads of Europe, and today, gem connoisseurs the world over, emeralds, more than any other precious gemstone, have sparked the eternal fires of our collective imagination.

Legends and lore

Spring is a time of growth and rejuvenation. Nothing reflects this more than the intense green shades of an emerald, May's birthstone.

Emeralds are regarded by many cultures as a symbol of personal development. It was once thought that emeralds possessed the power to soothe the soul and sharpen wit.

Some people believe that wearing an emerald brings wisdom, growth, and patience. And as any couple would agree, all of these qualities are essential for lasting love. This may explain why a gift of emerald is considered symbolic of love and devotion. Emeralds are even believed to change color upon infidelity.

EMERALD:	May's birthstone
Major Sources:	Afghanistan, Brazil, China, Colombia, Pakistan, Russia, Zambia & Zimbabwe
Colors Found:	Green
Family:	Beryl: $Be_3Al_2Si_6O_{18}$
Hardness:	7.5 to 8
Refractive Index:	1.56–1.60; Uniaxial (−)
Specific Gravity:	2.67–2.78
Crystal System:	Hexagonal

Emeralds have long been thought to possess healing powers. While today, we know that they are not a cure for all medical and psychological problems, many people still use emeralds to soothe their eyes and bring them good health. In fact, green has long been considered a soothing color, and it is no coincidence that the "green room" in theaters and TV studios is supposed to relax a performer after the stress and eyestrain of studio and stage lights.

A truly ancient gemstone, there is archaeological evidence that the Babylonians may have been marketing emeralds as early as 4000 BC.

The history of Egyptian emeralds dates back over 4,000 years. Located in Egypt's eastern desert region, ancient miners braved extreme heat, scorpions, and snakes to search for the "green fire." Interestingly, Greek miners once labored in the Egyptian desert for Alexander the Great.

The ancient mines of Egypt were rediscovered in 1818 by the French explorer Caillaud. Finding the mine with the help of the Egyptian government, he noted that emeralds were probably mined there long after the kings and queens of Egypt ruled the land.

The Egyptians were known to engrave emeralds with the symbol for foliage—to represent eternal youth, burying these jewels with their dead.

Emeralds were said to be the favorite gem of Cleopatra. She often wore lavish emerald jewelry and bestowed visiting dignitaries with large emeralds carved with her likeness on them when they departed Egypt.

Egyptian emeralds were first mined some 2,000 years before Cleopatra's birth. During her reign, she claimed these emerald mines as her own, as well as the world's oldest source of peridot, the fog-wrapped desert isle of Zeberget (St. John's Island). Zeberget peridot has a uniquely emerald-like color due to its high nickel content. This is probably why many of Cleopatra's "emeralds" were later found to be peridot.

The ancient Romans associated emerald with fertility and rebirth, dedicating it to Venus, their goddess of love and beauty. The Roman historian Pliny the Elder once said of emeralds, "nothing green is greener," and recorded that the Roman Emperor Nero, while presiding over gladiatorial fights, wore spectacles made of emeralds. However, gemologists now believe that this was highly unlikely, as the ancient Egyptian emerald produced crystals of insufficient size and clarity needed for such an instrument. Historians now believe that Fire Beryl™ was probably the gem used.

The legends and lore surrounding emeralds would not be complete without recounting the infamous stories of the Conquistadors. Hernando Cortés started his campaign against the Aztecs in 1519, and Francisco Pizarro commenced his military operation against the Incas in 1526. When Cortés planted the Spanish flag on Aztec soil, he snatched from the defeated Emperor Moctezuma an enormous, pyramid-shaped emerald—so big it could be seen from 300 feet away.

Just the facts

The green color of emeralds is unparalleled in the gem kingdom. Its beautiful green, combined with its rarity, makes emerald one of the world's most valuable gemstones. Interestingly, its name comes from the Greek word *smaragdos*, meaning "green gem."

Emeralds are members of the beryl family of minerals. Minute traces of chromium, vanadium, and iron give them their famous "green fire." The green crystals grow slowly within metamorphic rocks and are restricted in size by the host rock, making large emeralds rare and costly.

Unlike other beryls, emeralds often contain inclusions and tiny fractures. These are commonly called *jardin*, from the French word for "garden," because of their resemblance to foliage. For emeralds, jardin is not looked on as a negative aspect (like it would be for some other gem varieties), but instead, it is considered part of emerald's character and can be used to assure the purchaser of a natural gemstone.

Although emerald is relatively hard and durable, it must be protected from harsh blows because the jardin found within makes it susceptible to breaking. The famous "emerald cut" was developed specifically for this gem to reduce the amount of pressure exerted during cutting.

Transparent emeralds are faceted in gem cuts for jewelry, while translucent material is cut and polished into cabochons and beads. *Trapiche emeralds* are also cut into cabochons, making exquisite jewelry pieces.

A very small number of emeralds display asterism and chatoyancy; these, too, are cut into cabochons.

When buying emeralds, the most important consideration is always color, with clarity and quality of cut playing second fiddle. Nevertheless, the brightness of the gemstone, which is somewhat determined by the cutting and clarity, is also an important factor.

Colombian emerald

Traditionally, deep green is the most desired color in emeralds. Paler emeralds are sometimes called green beryl.

As emeralds from different locations can vary slightly in appearance, some of the main sources and varieties are detailed below.

Colombian emerald

Known for their vivid green color, Colombian emeralds are usually of exceptional quality. Colombia is, by tradition and lore, the finest modern source for emeralds.

With each comprised of many individual mines, the three historically significant areas of emerald mining in Colombia are Muzo, Coscuez, and Chivor.

Muzo mine

The famed Muzo mines lie 100 miles north of Bogotá. Emerald crystals from Muzo tend to have more saturated color than either Coscuez or Chivor. They are considered some of the finest emerald mines in the world.

Trapiche emeralds are extremely unusual, rare, prized forms of emeralds only found in the Muzo mining district of Colombia. Star-shaped rays that emanate from their centers in a hexagonal pattern characterize them. These rays appear much like asterism, but unlike asterism, they are not caused by light reflection from tiny, parallel inclusions. They are instead caused by black carbon impurities that happen to form in the same pattern.

Trapiche emerald

Coscuez mine

The emerald crystals of Coscuez tend to exhibit a very wide range of colors, but, unfortunately, they also tend to be more included than those from Muzo.

Chivor mine

Chivor emeralds are best known for their bluish cast, and they generally have fewer inclusions and a lighter color than either Coscuez or Muzo emeralds. The Chivor mining area is the smallest of the three and is separate from Muzo and Coscuez, which lie adjacent to each other.

Brazilian emerald

While Colombian emeralds are known for their vivid green color, Brazilian emeralds are known for their variety of color, ranging from light green to medium-dark blue-green.

Emeralds were first discovered in Brazil about 500 years ago, after the arrival of the Portuguese. However, it was only in 1963 when the first samples with commercial value were found in Bahia, close to the town of Paraíso do Norte in northern Brazil, effectively wiping out the notion that Brazil had no real "green fire" of its own.

Pakistani emerald

While an extremely harsh climate prevents the mining of emerald deposits at higher altitudes, at lower elevations in the Swat Valley of Pakistan lie the Gujar Kili mine and the ancient, historically significant Mingora mine (e.g., ancient Roman earrings featuring Mingora emeralds have been discovered). Severe weather conditions restrict operations during winter, making the hand-dug output very limited. The Pakistani government tightly controls the mining of emeralds from relatively new deposits discovered in 1960 in the Himalayan mountains.

Brazilian emerald

Russian emerald

Russian emerald is long prized for its breathtaking crystal clarity, green fire, and forest green hues.

According to history, a Russian peasant, Maxim Stefanovitch Koshevnikov, discovered Russian emerald in 1830, in the roots of a tree that had been felled in a storm on the Tokovaya River near Ekaterinburg, in Russia's Ural Mountains. Despite this, rumors persist that Russia actually supplied emeralds long before the Spaniards discovered the famous Colombian emerald in the late 16th century. These legends even go as far as to suggest that the Scythian emeralds mentioned by Pliny the Elder in his *Historia Naturalis* came from the Urals.

Russian emerald

Rising to fame in the 19th century, the largest and best-known source of Russian emerald is the Mariinsky (St. Mary's) mine. This mine was discovered in 1833 near the village of Malysheva. The deposits were nationalized after World War I, and emerald mining soon ceased when Malysheva became a military security zone. Russian emeralds almost entirely disappeared; thankfully, they are now back, and we are delighted to offer an amazing selection to JTV customers. Russian emerald is mined from a large beryllium deposit and is one of the deepest colored-gem mines in the world. Less than half a percent of the rough crystals mined are suitable for faceting. As a result, Russian emeralds are a "must have" for any true emerald connoisseur.

Zambian emerald

Zambian emeralds are of very high quality. Although Zambia has the world's second largest emerald deposit, it is substantially underdeveloped and primarily restricted to artisanal mines near Kagem, Kitwe, Miku, and Mufulira in remote northern Zambia. As basic hand tools are mainly used to mine Zambian emerald, this limits supply, increasing its rarity and value. Zambian emerald is extracted from talc-magnetite schists Zambian miners call *paidas* (when it is unaltered) and *chikundula* (when it is weathered). They call small emerald crystals that may be indicative of bigger crystals *ubulunga*.

Zambian emerald

FELDSPAR

While *feldspar* is the most abundant mineral family in the world, gem-quality crystals are scarce, coveted, and spectacularly beautiful, often possessing rare optical effects such as adularescence, aventurescence, and iridescence. Many feldspar gems only occur in isolated deposits and are far rarer than better-known gems such as diamond, ruby, or sapphire.

The name *feldspar* comes from the German *feldt spat*, meaning "field stone," because when feldspar weathers, it releases plant nutrients like potassium, which enrich soil.

Just the facts

There is a wide variety of feldspar gem types, and some are confusingly similar in appearance and composition. The various trade names can also confuse, as the same name is often applied to gemstones that are somewhat different in appearance, origin, and composition. Amazonite, andesine, labradorite, moonstone, orthoclase, and sunstone are all members of the feldspar family.

The two main subgroups are the alkali (potassium) group and the plagioclase group.

ALKALI:	Composition	Notable Gem Examples
Orthoclase	Monoclinic: $KAlSi_3O_8$	Moonstone
Sanidine	Monoclinic: (K, Na) $AlSi_3O_8$	Rarely seen as a gem
Microcline	Triclinic: $KAlSi_3O_8$	Amazonite
Anorthoclase	Triclinic: $(Na, K)AlSi_3O_8$	Rarely seen as a gem

PLAGIOCLASE:	Series from albite ($NaAlSi_3O_8$) through anorthite ($CaAl_2Si_2O_8$) and includes:	
Albite	100–90% albite	Moonstone
Oligoclase	90–70% albite	Sunstone, red
Andesine	70–50% albite	Yellow, orange, red, green
Labradorite	50–30% albite	Spectrolite, moonstone, sunstone, colorless, yellow, red, green
Bytownite	30–10% albite	Reddish, rarely cut
Anorthite	10–0% albite	Pale yellow, rarely cut

FELDSPAR:	Optical effects
Major Sources:	Brazil, China, India, Madagascar, Sri Lanka, Tanzania, Tibet & USA
Colors Found:	Various
Family:	Feldspar
Hardness:	6 to 6.5
Refractive Index:	1.51–1.57; Biaxial (+ or −)
Specific Gravity:	2.56–2.75

Orthoclase

FLUORITE

Deriving its name from the Latin word *fluere*, meaning "to flow" (in reference to its low melting point), *fluorite* is known as "the world's most colorful gemstone."

Fluorite, from which we get the word *fluorescent*, crosses the entire color spectrum, from deep purple to crimson red, blue to green (chrome fluorite), and frosty orange to lemon yellow. Fluorite is one of the more famous fluorescent minerals. Many specimens strongly fluoresce in a great variety of colors.

Fluorite crystal

Legends and lore
According to crystal healers, fluorite is a Third Eye gem, bringing rationality to intuitive qualities. It is believed to offer a stabilizing energy, facilitating order, balance, and healing. Fluorite is also believed to be excellent for fostering clarity of mind, objectivity, concentration, and meditation.

Just the facts
Due to its glassy luster, fluorite is highly coveted. It is the natural crystalline form of calcium fluoride and often forms beautiful cube-shaped crystals; it is a transparent to translucent mineral. When pure, fluorite is colorless; however, it usually contains impurities that color it. The most common colors are violet, blue, green, yellow, brown, pink, and bluish black.

FLUORITE:	Comes in many colors
Major Sources:	Brazil & India
Colors Found:	Various
Family:	Fluorite: CaF_2
Hardness:	4
Refractive Index:	1.43; SR
Specific Gravity:	3.00–3.25
Crystal System:	Cubic

Arguably, the most popular color for fluorite is a deep purple that can rival amethyst in its finest examples. Indeed, fluorite/amethyst comparisons are often used to show that color cannot be relied upon as a gemstone identification test.

An eye-catching phenomenon of fluorite is its distinctive multicolored banding. Chunky fluorite bead strands optimize this exceptional effect. Interestingly, the "blue john" variety, mined in England, that possesses curved bands of blue, purple, violet, yellow, and white has been used as an ornamental gem since Roman times.

Color-change fluorite is mined in Bihar, India. This material shows a dramatic change from green to purple. (Color-change gems are those that distinctly change their color when viewed under two different light sources.)

Pear-shaped Brazilian violet color-change fluorite

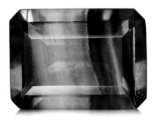

Emerald-cut Chinese bi-colored fluorite

GARNET

GARNET

Garnet **has a history spanning more than 5,000 years. Deriving its name from the Latin word for "seed,"** *granatus,* **garnet was so named because of its similar color to pomegranate seeds.**

From the svelte necklines of Abyssinian princesses to the powdered décolletage of Marie Antoinette, the captivating mystique of garnets has made them a timeless symbol of feminine beauty. The imaginative lure of this "queen of gems" intoxicates the senses.

Understanding garnets

Garnets are a group of related mineral species with essentially the same crystal structure but varying in chemical composition. Garnets rarely occur in nature as pure end members. Instead, a natural garnet's composition typically falls somewhere in between the pure ideals of other garnet members.

Group	Species	Pure Types	Mixed Types
Pyralspites	Almandine: $Fe_3Al_2Si_3O_{12}$	Almandine (red, from Fe)	Rhodolite (pyrope & almandine)
	Pyrope: $Mg_3Al_2Si_3O_{12}$	Pyrope (colorless, but never found pure; colored red by Fe)	Mozambique (pyrope & almandine)
	Spessartine: $Mn_3Al_2Si_3O_{12}$	Spessartine (orange, from Mn)	Malaia (intermediate composition range between spessartine & pyrope) & color change
Ugrandites	Andradite: $Ca_3Fe_2Si_3O_{12}$	Demantoid (green), topazolite (yellow)	Mali (andradite & grossular)
	Grossular: $Ca_3Al_2Si_3O_{12}$	Tsavorite (green), hessonite (orange) & other colors	Mali (andradite & grossular)
	Uvarovite: $Ca_3Cr_2Si_3O_{12}$	Green, from Cr	

Legends and lore

Garnet's associated symbolism with pomegranates has been longstanding. Interestingly, several ancient pieces of jewelry have been unearthed that are studded with tiny red garnets in cluster-like patterns reminiscent of pomegranates. The fruit is associated with eternity in Greek mythology and mentioned specifically in the legend of Hades' abduction of Persephone.

Garnet has long been connected with fire and was thought to possess the ability to illuminate the sky at night. Today, the gem remains a symbol of faith, truth, and light. This story from *Grimm's Fairy Tales* nicely presents this association:

> "Once upon a time an elderly lady came upon an injured bird. Taking the bird home with her, she nursed it back to health until one day it flew away. Although the lady thought she'd never see it again, it returned to her house with a garnet that she put by her bedside. To her surprise, she awoke every night to see it shining as bright as a torch, illuminating the bird's gratitude for her kindness."

According to Jewish legends, during the great flood a radiant garnet guided the way for Noah, ultimately leading his ark to salvation. For Muslims, garnets are believed to illuminate the fourth heaven.

Garnet jewelry was buried with Norsemen to light their passage to Valhalla, and it was also used to light the palace of Abyssinia's monarch.

The Crusaders set garnets into their armor, believing that the gems' power would lead them to safety. During the Middle Ages, garnets were also believed to draw out negativity, ward off harm, and increase well being, chivalry, loyalty, and honesty.

In the Middle Ages, receiving garnet as a gift was considered good luck; however, if ever stolen, it was bad luck for the thief. It was also believed that a garnet's loss of luster was a sign of impending doom.

Although garnet was the "fashion gem" of the 18th and 19th centuries, the inadequacy of available tests often resulted in it being confused with dark ruby. Jewelry set with garnets from Czechoslovakia was particularly admired, and although today, the garnets are mined elsewhere, Bohemian-style garnet jewelry has retained its popularity.

In 1912, garnets were made the official birthstone for January by the American National Association of Jewelers. They were also the gemstone for Aquarians and a traditional gift for 2nd and 6th wedding anniversaries.

GARNET:	January's birthstone
Major Sources:	India, Kenya, Madagascar, Mali, Mozambique, Namibia, Nigeria, Russia, Sri Lanka & Tanzania
Colors Found:	Various
Family:	Garnet
Hardness:	6.5 to 7.5
Refractive Index:	1.72–1.94; SR
Specific Gravity:	3.62–4.30
Crystal System:	Cubic

Just the facts

Even though there are many types of garnets (including trade and historic, there are currently 38 known garnet names), appearing in as many colors, when you say *garnets,* most people automatically think of small, dark red gemstones. In fact, garnets offer enough variety for every taste and can consequently keep up with the fast pace of changes in fashion.

Andradite garnet

Named after the Brazilian geologist José B. de Andrada e Silva, andradite is one of three garnets in the ugrandite series. (The other two are uvarovite and grossularite.) Varieties of andradite include topazolite (yellow), melanite (black), and demantoid (green). One very special variety called *rainbow garnet* exhibits a stunning multicolor iridescence and is normally free form in shape with minimal facets. This is due to the variable range and depth of the iridescent layers. In general, andradite garnets offer the highest dispersion within the garnet group. When fashioned with modified brilliant cuts, both the fire and brilliance are improved.

Andradite garnet

Champagne garnet

A distinctive and very attractive color variety of Malaia garnet, champagne garnet is, in fact, a mixture of pyrope and spessartine garnet and is mined in Tanzania's Umba Valley.

Champagne garnet

Color-change garnet

Color-change garnets are some of the rarest, most interesting, and phenomenal of all gemstones. An extremely rare variety of Malaia garnet, color-change garnet is, in fact, a mixture of pyrope and spessartine garnet. Comparatively, it is slightly rarer than alexandrite, and it is a constant struggle to get enough quantity to craft lines of jewelry. As our selection is usually relatively limited, it is one of those gems that discerning customers should purchase when they see it, as it simply isn't always available.

While color-change garnets have been reported since the early 1970s, they were only noted as a curiosity by a very small number of gemologists and gem collectors because of very limited quantities and colors that were viewed more as strange rather than beautiful. This situation dramatically changed in 1987 when Russian alexandrite-like color-change garnets were discovered in Tanzania's Umba Valley. Since that time, the gemstones have become increasingly coveted by gem collectors and jewelry connoisseurs alike. Historically, color-change gems have been popular since the discovery of alexandrite in the 19th century.

**Color-change garnet
(daylight and incandescent light)**

The Madagascan varieties generally display greens (including bluish greens) when viewed under sunlight, changing to raspberries (reddish purples) under candlelight. The Tanzanian varieties generally display khaki olive limes when viewed under sunlight, changing to orange crimson reds under candlelight. However, other color varieties of color-change garnet exist—in daylight, their color ranges from shades of green, beige, brown, gray, and blue (in hues more synonymous with blue spinel rather than sapphire), but in incandescent light, they appear a reddish or purplish/pink color. The color change can be intense and equal to the color change of top-quality alexandrite. As a result, color-change garnets can easily be mistaken for them.

Discovered in the late 1990s, Madagascan color-change garnet is from Bekily, in southern Madagascar, while Tanzanian color-change garnet is, today, predominately sourced from Tunduru, in Tanzania's Ruvuma region. It is also found in some parts of the United States, Russia, Turkey, and Sri Lanka (in very small quantities).

Color-change garnets are not usually found in large sizes. According to one source, the largest known faceted color-change garnet weighed 9.5 carats. The most dramatic color changes in color-change garnets are due to high amounts of vanadium (in contrast to chromium, which causes color change in alexandrite), although chromium is responsible for the color change in some of them. The existence of additional coloring agents, such as manganese, can also cause some of the more delicate colors in this garnet variety.

Demantoid garnet

A favorite of the famous Russian goldsmith, Karl Fabergé, demantoid garnet is one of the most desirable of all colored gemstones and extremely rare. Discovered in 1855 in the Russian central Ural Mountains at two alluvial deposits, it was first assumed to be emerald. It even took the name *Uralian emerald* until gemologists took a closer look. A color variety of andradite garnet, the name *demantoid* originates from the old German word *demant*, meaning "diamond-like," because of luster and dispersion that yield a fire even higher than diamonds.

Demantoid garnet

Some Russian demantoid garnets have golden byssolite strands that form beautiful patterns similar to the tail of a horse (thus, they are commonly known as "horsetail inclusions"). Those with prominent horsetail inclusions are particularly coveted. While small-scale mining reportedly recommenced in Russia in 1991, most demantoid garnets are sourced from relatively new deposits beneath the scorched desert sands of Namibia. Due to a fire greater than that of diamond, demantoid garnet is an absolute "must have" for any serious collector.

Hessonite garnet

A variety of grossular garnet, hessonite comes in two colors: golden and cinnamon (commonly known as the *cinnamon stone*). A perfectly colored hessonite is a bright golden orange that resembles a combination of honey and orange with an internal fire. Some hessonites have tints of red and brown.

Hessonite has been popular for thousands of years. The ancient Greeks and Romans used it in jewelry, cameos, and intaglios (figures cut into gems to make the designs depressed below the surfaces, whereas in cameos, the figures rise above the surfaces). Interestingly, hessonite's name comes from the Greek word *esson*, meaning "inferior," because it is slightly softer than other garnet varieties. However, please don't be put off by the origin of its name. It is still durable and perfectly suited to jewelry.

Hessonite garnet

Widely used in Vedic astrology, hessonite is known as *gomedha* in Hindi. The ancient Hindus believed that it was formed from the fingernails of the great demon Vala, which were scattered in the lakes of the East. Vedic astrologers believe that when set in gold, the gem is a powerful talisman that increases your lifespan and happiness.

Hessonite is common in the gem gravels of Sri Lanka, and practically all hessonite is obtained from this locality, although it is also found in Africa.

While the clearest gems are most prized, inclusions in hessonite are common, with unique toffee-like streaks giving hessonite an oily or even glass-like appearance.

Malaia garnet

Discovered in the mid 1960s in Tanzania's Umba Valley, this red-orange to pink-orange variety of garnet was originally thought to be spessartine.

Actually a mixture of pyrope, almandine, and spessartine, Malaia garnets are lively gems that exhibit sparkling red flashes. Once discovered not to be spessartine, it aptly became known by the Swahili word *malaia*, meaning "outcast."

Malaia garnets are available in numerous shades of orange, ranging from soft peach to intense reddish orange.

Mali garnet

Mali garnet is one of the latest discoveries in the garnet family. Mali garnet is an attractive and very interesting rare mixture of andradite and grossular that was only discovered in late

Malaia and Mali garnets

1994 at the Sandaré Mine in Mali's Kayes region (Diakon Arrondissement). Extremely rare, Mali garnets are a bright, uniform, light yellowish green color.

Merelani mint garnet

Long regarded as a source of the finest colored gems, it is no surprise that Tanzania is home to some of the world's most coveted garnets. Displaying a stunning mint green color, luster, sparkly brilliance, and excellent durability, the rare Merelani mint garnet is a relatively new gemstone whose popularity is only limited by its scarcity.

Named for where it is mined and its color, Merelani mint garnet was first discovered around 1998 in the same area as tanzanite (Merelani Hills, Arusha region, Tanzania). It is basically a different hue of its better-known relative, tsavorite (grossular garnet). Extremely scarce, Merelani mint garnet is always relatively small in size (under one carat) and is usually included with bubbles and/or silk. Not surprisingly, when clean, it increases in value.

Formed in metasomatic conditions (the process by which the chemical composition of a rock is changed by interaction with fluids), it is typically extracted directly from metamorphic rocks. Similar to tanzanite, it is found in association with graphite.

Stunning green garnets have historically always been in high demand, and Merelani mint garnet is coveted for a very good reason—few garnets have such a brilliant appeal.

Merelani mint garnet

Mozambique garnet

Originating in the east African nation it is named after, Mozambique garnet is famed for its high quality and wonderfully warm red color.

The gem is a mixture of pyrope and almandine garnet, similar in color to rhodolite garnet, but slightly redder and darker.

Pyrope garnet

Hear the word "garnet" and what invariably comes to mind is the image of the deep red pyrope garnet belonging to the pyralspites family. Pyrope comes from the Greek word *pyropos*, meaning "fiery eyed."

Fine pyrope garnets may be visually confused with dark rubies. It was the "fashion gem" of the 18th and 19th centuries, and many rubies of this period were later found to be pyrope garnets.

Mozambique and pyrope garnets

Rhodolite garnet

The name *rhodolite* is taken from the Greek *rho'don* and *lithos*, which literally translate to "rose stone." This is easy to see because the gem possesses a color reminiscent of the rhododendron flower. Its name was first used in the late 19th century to describe garnets discovered in North Carolina.

Unusually striking, rhodolite is a naturally occurring blend of almandine and pyrope garnet. While raspberry is its most prized color, it is also found in shades of pink through lavender.

Rhodolite is typically found as water-worn pebbles in alluvial deposits, but it is also occasionally mined directly from host metamorphic rock. The most spectacular rhodolite is mined in Sri Lanka, Zimbabwe, and from a relatively new deposit in the Kangala area of Tanzania that was discovered in 1987. Since then, gorgeous raspberry-hued rhodolite has been found in other regions of Tanzania, including Ruvuma, Mtwara, and Lindi.

Tough, durable, never enhanced, and easily cleaned, rhodolite is ideal for jewelry. Due to its bright, transparent clarity, it is often cut into fantasy shapes.

Rhodolite garnet

Spessartine garnet

Mandarin garnets are the intensely bright color varieties of the rare orange-red spessartine garnet, also known as *spessartite*.

Spessartine garnet is named after its first discovery in Spessart, Bavaria, in the mid-1800s. Once an extremely rare gem, it is now enjoying a newfound popularity.

In 1991, Mandarin garnets were discovered embedded in mica in northwest Namibia, where the Kunene River borders Namibia and Angola. In 1994, new deposits were unearthed in southwest Nigeria. Soon after, Tanzania, the powerhouse of African gems, yielded deposits at the fabled gemstone mines of Arusha and Lelatema.

Although initially called *kunene spessartine* or *hollandine*, the evocative name *Mandarin garnet* was soon adopted.

Three different flavors of spessartine garnet

Star garnet

A highly unusual form of garnet is the rare, four-rayed almandine star garnet. While almandine garnets (also known as *almandites*) are the most common variety of garnets, those displaying the star are not at all common. Available in deep reds, they are found in Nigeria and Tanzania.

Asterism, or the star effect, is a reflection effect that appears as two or more intersecting bands of light crossing the surface of a gem.

Tsavorite garnet

For some, the '60s swung; for gemologists, they rocked. The decade that had most people looking to the sky for Lucy's diamonds had gemologists transfixed by a myriad of precious gemstones hailing from Africa's arid savannas: fancy sapphires, rubies, tourmalines, tanzanites, and a plethora of gorgeous colored garnets, among them a brilliant green grossular garnet called *tsavorite*. Tsavorite, East Africa's beautiful green gemstone, is rightful heir to the title "the king of garnets." Some 40 years after its discovery, it has comfortably established itself as one of the world's most beautiful, precious, and desirable gemstones. Comparable in

Tsavorite garnet

scarcity to demantoid garnet, it is extremely rare. In fact, it is so rare that it might be unavailable in future years.

First discovered in 1967 by the now-legendary Scottish geologist Campbell R. Bridges, tsavorite has quickly found favor as a precious colored gem of choice. Bridges first discovered it in Tanzania, but in those days, getting an export permit to take the gems out was impossible. Aided by the local Maasai and Kikuyu tribesmen, Bridges persisted in his search. This time, he turned his attention to the neighboring country of Kenya. In 1971, he discovered tsavorite for a second time in Kenya's Tsavo region. Life in Africa's bush is dangerous, and the Tsavo region is well known as the domain of man-eating lions and poachers. In order to protect himself from predators and brigands, Bridges was forced to live in a tree house. And because he didn't want his treasure to be stolen, he cunningly used the locals' fear of snakes by placing a python in amongst the tsavorite rough.

Tsavorite eventually found its way to America, where Henry Platt of Tiffany & Co. named the gemstone, basing its name on the famous Tsavo National Park in Kenya. Tsavorite took the world by storm, and interest increased dramatically when, in 1974, Tiffany's started a special campaign promoting it, making it well known in the USA. International promotional campaigns followed, and soon, global demand for tsavorite reached epic proportions.

While tsavorite was once being mined in 40 different areas throughout Tanzania and Kenya, only four mining ventures are still producing commercial quantities. Although some 50 deposits have been found in Kenya, Tanzania, Madagascar, and even Zambia, only a handful of small mines are viable. This is because tsavorite is notoriously difficult to mine, requiring a good understanding of geology. Seams suddenly disappear, giving no indication where to look next, and its crystals are often found inside quartz or scapolite "potatoes" that must be cracked open to reveal the tsavorite.

The gem's intense green color, similar to that of fine emerald, is due to the presence of vanadium in the host rock. Like all garnets, tsavorite possesses few inclusions, and its high refractive index results in a superb brilliance. While by no means an absolute, Kenyan tsavorite generally possesses deeper color saturation than those from Tanzania.

Umbalite garnet
Umbalite garnet is an attractive, light pinkish purple garnet that was first unearthed in Tanzania's Umba Valley in 1978. It is a cocktail of pyrope and almandine, with small traces of spessartine garnet. Production of this unusual gem material has been irregular, and it is highly sought after by connoisseurs of fine gemstones.

Umbalite garnet

GOSHENITE

While most members of the beryl family, including emerald and aquamarine, are famous for their colors, *goshenite* is quite the opposite. It is prized for its *absence* of color. Even though sources are limited, it is still very affordable and a must-have for any gem collector.

Legends and lore

The name *goshenite* is derived from the location of its first discovery, Goshen, Massachusetts. The gem is also known as *white beryl* or *lucid beryl*.

They are enduringly popular gemstones and have been used in jewelry since antiquity. The ancient Greeks even used them as lenses in the first spectacles.

Just the facts

Interestingly, pure beryl is colorless, with traces of different metallic elements being responsible for this gem family's great color range.

Since beryl's color varieties are caused by metallic elements, and pure beryl is colorless, one could assume that goshenite is beryl in its purest form. However, this is not technically correct as some metallic elements in natural goshenite actually inhibit the colors that result from other metallic elements that may also be present.

Madagascan goshenite

GOSHENITE:	Also known as white beryl
Major Sources:	Afghanistan, Brazil, Colombia, Pakistan, South Africa & USA
Colors Found:	Colorless
Family:	Beryl: $Be_3Al_2Si_6O_{18}$
Hardness:	7.5 to 8
Refractive Index:	1.56–1.60; Uniaxial (−)
Specific Gravity:	2.66–2.87
Crystal System:	Hexagonal

Fancy-cut goshenite

GREEN AMETHYST

GREEN AMETHYST (PRASIOLITE)

Green amethyst **can be a confusing gem. It is traded under a variety of names and is even sometimes mistaken for other gemstones such as peridot and tourmaline. The green variety of quartz, green amethyst is also known as** *vermarine, green quartz,* **and** *lime citrine*—**or by its gemological name,** *prasiolite.* **Although reasonably affordable, it is unusual and remains a collector's gemstone.**

Green amethyst is mostly mined in Brazil. Its gemological name is derived from the Greek words *prason,* meaning "leek" (due to its color similarities with the vegetable), and *lithos,* meaning "stone."

Legends and lore
Green amethyst is believed by crystal healers to facilitate the gap between the physical and spiritual aspects of life, attracting prosperity through strengthening the mind, emotions, and will.

Just the facts
Although quartz of sufficient beauty to be set into jewelry is not available in great abundance, the gem itself is found in many geological environments and is a component of almost every rock type. It is also the most varied in terms of varieties, colors, and forms. Quartz gemstones are often separated into two groups, based on the size of their individual crystals. Green amethyst is a macrocrystalline quartz (large crystal), and this group includes many popular gemstones such as amethyst, citrine, and ametrine.

GREEN AMETHYST:	Green variety of quartz
Major Sources:	Brazil
Colors Found:	Shades of green
Family:	Quartz: SiO_2
Hardness:	7
Refractive Index:	1.54–1.55; Uniaxial (+)
Specific Gravity:	2.65
Crystal System:	Trigonal

All forms of quartz are piezoelectric (when heated or rubbed, they create an electrical charge, becoming a magnet that attracts lightweight objects), making for important applications in electronics. (Tourmaline is the only other gemstone that possesses this property.)

With beautiful colors ranging from pastel to deep forest green, green amethyst is a tough gemstone, making it ideal for everyday wear.

Oval quantum-cut prasiolite

HELIODOR

HELIODOR

First discovered in Rossing, Erongo, in western Namibia in 1910, *heliodor* was named from the Greek *helios* and *doron*, meaning "gift from the sun."

Displaying characteristic yellow to yellowish greens (similar to olive oil), heliodor is a variety of beryl, the "mother of gemstones." Interestingly, as an allochromatic gem, pure beryl is colorless. Traces of different elements are responsible for beryl's great color range.

Legends and lore

Among crystal healers, heliodor has traditionally been used as a charm to promote compassion, sincerity, and sympathy. It is also believed by some to enhance one's intuition and to improve one's communicative abilities.

Just the facts

Heliodor's main characteristic is its color, which is produced when iron replaces some aluminum in the crystal structure. The color depends on the relative concentration and location of iron within the beryl crystal structure. However, the shade may vary, and it is often difficult to establish a dividing line between heliodor, golden beryl, and yellow beryl. Originally, golden beryl found in Namibia was called *heliodor*, but today, the name is used to describe the yellowish green varieties of beryl, with the golden colors called *golden beryl* and the yellow colors called *yellow beryl*. However, please be aware that these demarcations are still confused by some sources.

Not surprisingly, heliodor was discovered in a pegmatite that also produced aquamarine, a beryl also colored by iron. Like aquamarine, the more intense colors frequently have more inclusions. Heliodor occurs primarily in granite pegmatites, and to a lesser extent, in granite cavities. Because of its relatively robust hardness and specific gravity, it is sometimes found in alluvial deposits.

Heliodor is famous for its perfect, six-sided prismatic hexagonal crystals that usually occur individually. These are often enormous, and some 26-foot, well-crystallized examples are known to have existed. Understandably, only very small amounts of these enormous crystals are of a sufficient quality to be used in jewelry.

HELIODOR:	Perfect, prismatic hexagonal crystals
Major Sources:	Brazil, Madagascar, Namibia, Nigeria, Russia & Ukraine
Colors Found:	Yellow to yellowish green
Family:	Beryl: $Be_3Al_2Si_6O_{18}$
Hardness:	7.5 to 8
Refractive Index:	1.56–1.60; Uniaxial (–)
Specific Gravity:	2.66–2.87
Crystal System:	Hexagonal

The gems can be faceted into various gem cuts, and some of the stones display chatoyancy (cat's-eye effect) when cut and polished into cabochons. When perfectly transparent six-sided crystals are discovered, they are sometimes set uncut in necklaces and pendants.

While the best heliodor traditionally hails from Namibia, beautiful specimens are also found in Minas Gerais, Brazil, the Ural Mountains in Russia, and the Ukraine. While heliodor's durability and summery colors make it well suited to jewelry, it is extremely difficult to find enough of it to craft lines of jewelry, particularly with respect to clean examples displaying intense colors and high luster (good cutting and polishing). Such material simply isn't available. Thus, despite its beauty, heliodor rarely makes an appearance in jewelry.

IOLITE

IOLITE

The name *iolite* comes from the Greek word *ios*, which means "violet." The gem iolite is transparent violet-blue, light blue, or yellow-gray. A pleochroic gem (different colors are displayed when the gemstone is viewed from different angles), it will show many colors in a single piece.

Legends and lore

According to ancient Scandinavian sagas, Norse navigators used thin pieces of iolite (their magical "sunstone") as the world's first polarizing filter. Looking through an iolite lens, they could determine the position of the sun on overcast days and navigate their boats safely. Hence, iolite is also known as the *Viking's compass* or *Viking's stone*. The story of the Viking compass triggered the curiosity of a 10-year-old boy, who just happened to be the son of the chief navigator of the Scandinavian Airline System, Jorgen Jensen. The "sunstone" described in Norse lore sounded similar to the twilight compass used by the boy's father at higher latitudes, where a magnetic compass is unreliable. His father's twilight compass was equipped with a polarizing filter that enables a navigator to locate the sun, even when it is behind the clouds, by light polarized by the atmosphere.

Intrigued by his son's observation, Jensen passed it onto Danish archaeologist Thorkild Ramskau, who immediately recognized its scientific implications. Collecting minerals found in Scandinavia, whose molecules are aligned similarly to the crystals in a polarizing filter, Ramskau put iolite (the gem variety of the mineral cordierite) to the test. Accompanying navigator Jorgen Jensen on a flight to Greenland, Ramskau kept track of the sun with a piece of iolite while Jensen used the twilight compass. Incredibly, his observations were accurate to within 2.5 degrees of the sun's true position.

IOLITE:	Also known as water sapphire
Major Sources:	India, Madagascar & Sri Lanka
Colors Found:	Violet-blue, light blue, or yellow-gray
Family:	Cordierite: $(Mg, Fe)_2Al_4Si_5O_{18}$
Hardness:	7 to 7.5
Refractive Index:	1.54–1.58; Biaxial (+ or –)
Specific Gravity:	2.58–2.66
Crystal System:	Orthorhombic

Known as "the gemstone of clear vision," when worn as an amulet, iolite was believed to have the power to guide lost sailors to the brilliance of the sun, allowing them to safely find their way home.

Just the facts

Iolite is a popular and interesting gemstone. It has a pretty violet-blue color that is unlike other gemstones, although it has been compared to light blue sapphires. It is for this reason that it is sometimes known as "water sapphire."

While an iolite necklace or iolite earrings are probably the best ways to showcase this gem's unique color, iolite rings are also desirable. After all, Iolite is a durable gem well suited to everyday wear.

Pleochroism is very pronounced in iolite and is seen as three different color shades in the same gem. When viewing iolite, the colors violet-blue, yellow-gray, and a light blue can be seen. When correctly faceted, the gem will show its best violet-blue color through its top or table. However, when viewed from another angle, the gem may display other colors.

JADE (NEPHRITE)

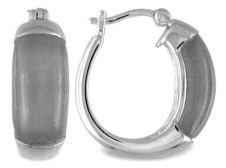

JADE (NEPHRITE)

For centuries, *nephrite jade* and the other jade type, *jadeite*, were considered one and the same. It was not until 1863, in France, that they were identified as different minerals with a similar appearance and properties.

The name *jade* was first used around the time of the Spanish conquest of Central and South America, and it is from the Spanish *piedra de ijada*, meaning "hip stone," as it was thought to cure kidney stones and other kidney ailments.

While jade was known as the "stone of heaven" in ancient China, the Chinese word for it, *yü*, is not generally used. Jade was excavated from the Kunlun Mountains of northwest China from 5000 BC, and even today, the country remains an important source for this gemstone.

Legends and lore

In Russia, jade has been mined and crafted since 3000 BC. Tsar Alexander III's sarcophagus was carved from it. For about 3,000 years. it has been highly prized by the Native Americans of British Columbia, Canada, who called it "greenstone." And for centuries, the New Zealand Maori have made beautiful nephrite carvings.

Just the facts

Nephrite is composed of silica and magnesia, and its color is determined by the amount of iron present in the mineral. A lesser iron content produces lighter colors, such as white, cream, yellow, gray, green, blue, red, brown, and lavender. A greater iron content produces the darker-colored nephrite, such as darker gray and darker green.

JADE:	One of the toughest gems
Major Sources:	Canada (BC), China, New Zealand, Russia & Taiwan
Colors Found:	Blue, brown, cream, green, gray, lavender, red, white & yellow
Family:	Amphibole: $Ca_2(Mg,Fe)_5(Si_4O_{11})_2(OH)_2$
Hardness:	6 to 6.5
Refractive Index:	1.60–1.63
Specific Gravity:	2.90–3.03
Crystal System:	Monoclinic (aggregate)

Nephrite has the highest tensile strength (toughness as opposed to hardness) of all natural gemstones—and even has a tensile strength greater than some steel. It is so strong that it cannot be chiseled. It must be ground using sharp abrasives.

Interestingly, less than 0.05% of nephrite extracted is of gem quality. It is typically not dyed, as it is less likely to take up dye or stains than jadeite. Older pieces benefit from polishing to retain their luster.

Green nephrite

JASPER

JASPER

Jasper **is an opaque and fine-grained variety of chalcedony quartz. It is typically found in red, yellow, brown, or green colors and generally has spots. Its name comes from the Latin word for jasper,** *iaspis,* **meaning "spotted stone," which probably also refers to the other types of chalcedony quartz.**

Jasper is normally cut as a cabochon and has traditionally been used as a gemstone for jewelry such as brooches, earrings, necklaces, pendants, intaglios (gems carved in negative relief), and cameos (gems carved in positive relief).

Legends and lore

Jasper was a favorite amulet gem in ancient times and is referenced in Greek, Hebrew, Assyrian, and Latin literature. For example, it is one of "the stones of fire" (Ezekiel 28:13–16) that was given to Moses at the mountain of God and said to possess the power to summon angels. Moses then decreed it mounted into a sacred breastplate for his brother, the high priest Aaron (Exodus 28:15–30). In the New Testament (Revelations 21:19), jasper is one of the 12 gemstones set in the foundations of the city walls of Jerusalem. As compiled by Andreas, Bishop of Caesurae, one of the earliest writers to tie the Apostles with the symbolism of the 12 gems of Jerusalem, jasper was denoted for the Apostle St. Peter.

In some Native American cultures, jasper is considered to be the symbolic blood of the earth, and was, thus, thought to be one of the best gems for connecting with the deep, stabilizing energies of the earth.

According to crystal healers, it is an intensely protective gem, acting to stabilize the aura and rid it of dysfunctional energy, thereby facilitating relaxation, contentment, and compassion.

JASPER:	Mentioned in the Bible
Major Sources:	India, Madagascar, Mexico & USA
Colors Found:	Brown, green, grayish white, pink, red, shades of bluish purple & yellow
Family:	Chalcedony quartz: SiO_2
Hardness:	6.5 to 7
Refractive Index:	1.54
Specific Gravity:	2.58–2.91
Crystal System:	Trigonal (aggregate)

Just the facts

Quartz gems are commonly separated into two groups based on the size of their individual crystals. The macrocrystalline quartz (large crystal) group includes popular gemstones such as amethyst, ametrine, and citrine. Cryptocrystalline quartz includes species whose individual crystals are too small to be easily distinguished. Apart from being a variety within the group, chalcedony is also a catchall term to describe cryptocrystalline quartz and includes jasper, as well as many other gems that have been coveted since antiquity.

Jasper

KORNERUPINE

Kornerupine **(also known as** *prismatine*) **was discovered in Fiskernaes, Greenland, in 1884, and it was named after the Danish geologist and explorer Andreas N. Kornerup (1857–1881). It is a rare gemstone well known for its pleochroism (different colors seen from different viewing angles) and its green color, which can be as intense as emerald.**

Legends and lore

Among crystal healers, kornerupine is considered a gemstone for teaching and communication. It is also said to help stabilize the emotional swings of manic depressives and assist in seeing through the false agreements in one's current reality.

Just the facts

A metamorphic mineral, kornerupine is a complex magnesium aluminum borosilicate whose crystals are often found in alluvial deposits collected behind rocks or in the bends of rivers. It is often deposited with other gems, including sapphire, chrysoberyl, ruby, topaz, garnet, zircon, diopside, andalusite, spinel, and iolite.

While kornerupine has a similar but slightly higher index of refraction than emerald, as well as its characteristic inclusions, the two gems are easily distinguished by kornerupine's pleochroism. Depending on the angle from which kornerupine is viewed, its colors can range from brown, colorless, green, greenish yellow, yellow, pink, or lavender. However, wherever possible, kornerupine is faceted on the green axis because this coloration is its rarest and most coveted hue.

KORNERUPINE:	Pleochroism
Major Sources:	Burma, Madagascar, Sri Lanka & Tanzania
Colors Found:	Brown, green & orange
Family:	Kornerupine: $Mg_3Al_6(Si,Al,B)_5O_{21}(OH)$
Hardness:	6.5 to 7
Refractive Index:	1.66–1.70; Biaxial (–)
Specific Gravity:	3.27–3.45
Crystal System:	Orthorhombic

The gem also occasionally exhibits chatoyancy, or the cat's-eye effect. When polished as cabochons, kornerupine can display a reflection effect that appears as a single bright band of light across its surface. This effect is caused by inclusions of fine, slender parallel fibers in the gem.

While kornerupine is a rare gem that used to be limited to collections, it is now becoming increasingly popular in jewelry due to its suitability for everyday wear.

Kornerupine

KUNZITE

KUNZITE

Discovered in California in 1902 (some sources say around 1877), *kunzite* was named after Tiffany's legendary gemologist and famous gemstone author, George Frederick Kunz.

Kunz described this durable pink gemstone as having two distinct properties: *phosphorescence* (where, like diamond, kunzite glows in a darkened room after it has been exposed to the sun's ultraviolet rays) and *pleochroism* (showing different colors when viewed from different directions). These phenomena are best seen in larger-sized gems set into jewelry like pendants, drop and chandelier earrings, and rings with open prong or bar settings that let light flow freely through them, accentuating kunzite's fire to full effect.

Kunzite radiates pure Parisian chic, revealing delicate pastel pinks, frosty lilacs, cool lavenders, hot fuchsias, and rich orchids under the warm glow of incandescent light (candlelight). Its subtle coloring perfectly complements *décolleté* evening wear and soft candlelight—hence, its colloquial name "the evening gemstone."

Legends and lore

Aside from their obvious physical beauty, pink gemstones possess potent metaphysical properties. Alternative healers use a multitude of pink gems in conjunction with the *heart chakra*. The fourth of seven energy points that run the course of the human body, the heart chakra is believed to carry the emotional sensibilities of love and compassion. Some believe that when the fourth chakra is blocked, we experience emotions such as anxiety, fear, anger, and frustration. Crystal healers use the properties of pink gems like pink tourmaline and kunzite to free the heart chakra from this negative energy. This alternative approach of enhancing the "power of pink" is a viewpoint shared and supported by traditional methods of medicine and psychology: "The color pink causes the brain to send signals that reduce the secretion of adrenalin, reducing the heart rate and consequently dissipating states of extreme excitement such as anger." (*Science Digest*, 1980)

Just the facts

The lithium in kunzite's chemical composition, lithium aluminum silicate, along with trace amounts of manganese, give it the wonderful pink colors that complement both autumn and spring wardrobes. As a member of the spodumene family, kunzite is closely related to hiddenite, a green variety of spodumene. It is an attractive gem but is extremely rare and, for the most part, is only known by collectors. Hiddenite was discovered in 1800 in Hiddenite, a city in Alexander County, North Carolina, USA. Both the city and the gem were named

KUNZITE:	Pleochroism
Major Sources:	Afghanistan, Brazil, Madagascar, Nigeria & Pakistan
Colors Found:	Shades of pink & yellow
Family:	Spodumene: $LiAlSi_2O_6$
Hardness:	6 to 7
Refractive Index:	1.66–1.68; Biaxial (+)
Specific Gravity:	3.15–3.21
Crystal System:	Monoclinic

after William Earl Hidden, a mineralogist and mining director from Newark, New Jersey, who was mining in the area. For many years, hiddenite was limited to North Carolina, but new deposits were recently discovered in Madagascar and Brazil. Green spodumene must contain trace amounts of chromium to be called *hiddenite*.

Spodumene's color is due to trace elements of iron (producing yellow to green), chromium (producing medium to deep green), or manganese (producing pink to lilac), all substituting for aluminum in the crystal structure. Some pink kunzite will naturally fade over time with exposure to strong light—another reason why it is known as an evening stone.

The name *spodumene* (named by José B. d'Andrada e Sylva in 1800) was derived from the Greek *spodumenos*, meaning "burnt to ashes," in reference to the light gray color of some spodumenes.

While kunzite is usually thought of as a pink to lilac gemstone, *yellow kunzite, mint kunzite,* and *white kunzite* are trade names used to describe yellow, light green, and colorless spodumene. Displaying delicate pastel lemon meringues, mint greens, and ice whites, these color varieties possess all the attributes of kunzite, albeit in other colors, providing kunzite lovers with delightful alternatives.

Kunzite is strongly pleochroic, meaning there is a color intensity variation and change when the crystal is viewed from different directions. A gem cutter must take great care to orient the gem in a position that accentuates its best color. The top and bottom of the crystal reveal the deepest colors, and our experienced gem cutters always take this into consideration when faceting kunzite for JTV.

From left to right, top to bottom: yellow kunzite, mint kunzite, hiddenite, kunzite, Brazilian kunzite, and Patroke kunzite (this rare color variety from Afghanistan is named for its mine)

KYANITE

Also called *disthene*, the name *kyanite* is derived from the Greek *kyanos*, meaning "blue." The most popular varieties display intensely beautiful colors reminiscent of top Ceylon and Kashmir sapphires. Although the name *kyanite* has been used since 1789, the gem was sold in Europe as sapphire until the turn of the 20th century.

Legends and lore

The powerful blue hues of kyanite have long been thought to inspire calmness, composure, serenity, loyalty, and respect.

Kyanite is used by alternative healers as a tool for meditation and relaxation. These healers use the stone to open the third eye chakra to enhance creativity, broaden perception, and to reach a better understanding of others. Kyanite is also said to foster tranquillity and believed to have a positive effect on dreams, visualization, and foresightedness.

Just the facts

Kyanite has perfect cleavage in one direction. This, combined with its varying hardness (it is extremely unusual, displaying two hardnesses within one gem), makes it a challenging gem to facet. Understandably, the cutting of it is an extremely important quality consideration.

Occurring in a variety of locations around the world, the best-quality kyanite hails from the Kali Gandaki region of west central Nepal.

KYANITE:	Perfect cleavage, varying hardness
Major Sources:	Nepal & Brazil
Colors Found:	Blue
Family:	Kyanite: Al_2SiO_5
Hardness:	4 to 7
Refractive Index:	1.71–1.73; Biaxial (–)
Specific Gravity:	3.53–3.70
Crystal System:	Triclinic

Kyanite

Nepalese kyanite and sterling silver ring

LABRADORITE

Labradorite is named after the Labrador peninsula in Canada, where it was discovered. Displaying brilliant pastels and deep golden colors, it even includes a variety colloquially known as "black rainbow," which features a spellbinding play of color. Labradorite is a stunning gemstone perfect for wardrobes in all seasons.

Legends and lore

Calling it *firestone* because of its captivating play of color, the Native Americans of Labrador attributed mystical qualities to labradorite, using the powdered gem as a magical potion to cure their ailments.

Interestingly, some modern mystics believe that labradorite is a gem that assists the practice of magic, unleashes the power of the imagination, and helps to overcome personal limitations.

LABRADORITE:	Labradorescence
Major Sources:	China, Finland, India & Madagascar
Colors Found:	Colorless, orange, red, smoke gray & yellow
Family:	Feldspar: $(Na,Ca)AlSi_3O_8$
Hardness:	6 to 6.5
Refractive Index:	1.55–1.57; Biaxial (+)
Specific Gravity:	2.65–2.75
Crystal System:	Triclinic

Just the facts

Labradorite is a sodium-rich variety of plagioclase feldspar. While transparent labradorite is relatively free from inclusions and appears red, orange, yellow, or colorless, the smoke gray varieties that show a rainbow-like color effect, or "iridescence," are most frequently used in jewelry.

Valued for its lustrous metallic reflections (*schiller*) that are said to resemble a butterfly's wing, this iridescence is aptly called *labradorescence* by gemologists and appears as stunning rainbow-colored reflections when light strikes the gem in a particular direction. Mainly caused by the interference of light from lattice distortions, cracks, or structural layers breaking up light into spectral colors, this effect often appears in violet, blue, green, yellow, gold, and even reddish orange tints.

Labradorite

Spectrolite, an extremely rare variety found previously only in Finland, but now also mined in India, can even display the complete color spectrum.

When appreciating the play of color in labradorite, observe the strength and intensity of the labradorescence when the gemstone is viewed from different angles. This may result in different colors being visible or even a range of colors all visible at the same time.

Yellow labradorite

LAPIS LAZULI

LAPIS LAZULI

The word *lapis* is the Latin word for "stone." The names *lazuli* and *lazurite* are derived from the Persian *lazhuward* and Latin *lazulum*, both meaning "blue" or "heaven." The full name *lapis lazuli* is often shortened to *lapis*.

Legend and lore

Few gems have such a long and storied history as lapis lazuli. Mentioned in the Sumerian epic of *Gilgamesh* (2650 BC) and in the book of Exodus in the Bible, lapis was also used by ancient Egyptians in religious ceremonies. Not only does lapis appear in various passages in the Egyptian *Book of the Dead*, but lapis items have also been found in royal tombs, including that of Tutankhamun. The ancient city of Ur had a thriving trade in lapis as early as the fourth millennium BC.

The Greeks and Romans used it as a reward for bravery, and the Romans believed lapis to be a powerful aphrodisiac. It was also employed by the Greeks and Romans for inlay work and for jewelry, amulets, and talismans. They named it *sapphirus* (blue), which is now used for the blue variety of corundum, sapphire.

When lapis was first introduced to Europe, it was called *ultramarinum*, meaning "beyond the sea." It was once powdered and mixed with oil to produce the pigment *ultramarine*, which is seen in the beautiful blues of Renaissance paintings. (Ultramarine has been made synthetically since 1828.)

In the Middle Ages, lapis was thought to keep the limbs healthy and free the soul from error, envy, and fear. During the 17th century, it was used in medicine to prevent miscarriages, epilepsy, and dementia.

Attributed with great curative and purifying properties, lapis allegedly points the way to enlightenment and aids in the opening of the third eye. Popular with ancient alchemists, it was used in medicine, cosmetics, and paintings. It was also believed to confer ability, success, divine favor, ancient wisdom, and cure sore throats. No wonder it was once as valuable as gold!

The Arab geographer Istakhri recorded a visit to the Afghanistan lapis mines in the 10th century, and Marco Polo visited and wrote about them in 1271.

LAPIS LAZULI:	Early gem and source of ultramarine
Major Sources:	Afghanistan, Chile & Colorado (USA)
Colors Found:	Blue
Family:	Lazurite (sodalite group)
Hardness:	5 to 6
Refractive Index:	1.50
Specific Gravity:	2.50–3.00

Faceted lapis lazuli

Just the facts

The famous lapis mines at Sar-e-Sang in Afghanistan's Badakhshan region have been in operation for some 7,000 years, making them among the oldest and longest-producing mines on the planet.

Lapis lazuli is actually a rock. Consisting mainly of lazurite, it also contains brassy pyrite specks and white calcite veins and patches. The best lapis is a rich, royal blue color with no visible calcite and just a light dusting of sparkling flecks of pyrite (fool's gold), adding to its mystical allure.

MALACHITE

Malachite **is named after the Greek word** *moloche,* **meaning "mallow," due to its similarity in color to mallow leaves.**

A secondary copper mineral, malachite is a popular gem that has light and dark vivid green bands. Many beautiful specimens of malachite contain special combinations with other minerals, such as azurite, cuprite, or chrysocolla.

Legends and lore

Malachite was admired by ancient Greek followers of the goddess Venus and thought to possess great powers.

In Rome, it was called the "peacock stone" and dedicated to the goddess Juno, who protects against lightning and other perils of nature. Continuing these ancient traditions to this day, some Italians wear malachite as protection against the evil eye.

Popular with the ancient Egyptians, according to legend, their hippo goddess Toeris (also associated with Hathor) wore a necklace of many beads, including malachite.

In antiquity, malachite was worn to detect impending danger, reportedly breaking into pieces when it was near. Hence, malachite was often regarded as "the guardian gem of travelers."

For modern crystal healers, malachite's powers include protection, power, peace, hope, love, and success in business.

Just the facts

Malachite's banded light and dark green designs are distinctive and unique, giving it a visual appearance unlike any other gem. It is arguably one of the most easily recognizable gemstones.

Its ability to mix with other minerals has led to malachite being unearthed in a wide array of attractive colors and patterns. These unique combinations create some truly intriguing gemstones.

Malachite

MALACHITE:	Also known as the peacock stone
Major Sources:	Namibia, Tanzania & Zambia
Colors Found:	Banded light & dark green
Family:	Malachite: $CuCO_3(OH)_2$
Hardness:	3.5 to 4
Refractive Index:	1.65–1.90
Specific Gravity:	3.25–4.10
Crystal System:	Monoclinic (aggregate)

MOONSTONE

MOONSTONE

Popular with the Romans, who thought it was formed out of moonlight, and in India, where it is considered a sacred zodiac gem, *moonstone* is one of the most coveted varieties of feldspar. Other names for it include *adularia* (a variety found in the European Alps near the Adula Group) and *selenite* (from the Greek *selene*, meaning "moon").

Legend and lore

Laced with superstitions, suspicion, humor, and romance, the earliest known traditions describe moonstone as having been set in the forehead of a four-handed Indian god who represented the moon. Partly from its unique color, partly from a superstition that represented it as feeling the influence of the deity whom it adorned, it first gained the name by which it continues to be known today in ancient India.

The gem's modern Western roots allegedly originate from the German word *mondstein* (moonstone) that was used to describe a lustrous variety of feldspar in the late 18th century.

This gem has always been revered because of its lunar attraction. In antiquity, it was believed to be the solidified rays of the moon, and the glimmering light within was thought to be the light of the good spirit that lived within it. In ancient Rome, moonstones were thought to change their appearance depending on the waning phases of the moon. They also thought that a picture of Diana, the goddess of the moon, could be seen in every moonstone.

In the Middle Ages, people thought that if you fell into a deep sleep after gazing into a moonstone, it would tell you the future. It has always been considered a feminine or "goddess" gem. One Asian legend points out that where there is a moon, there is no rain, and so the name *moonstone* means "no tears."

Moonstone is a highly prized gift for lovers because it is believed to arouse tender passion. According to another legend, a moonstone placed in the mouth while the moon is full gives lovers the power to read their futures together. In antiquity, men also used it to predict the future by placing it in their mouths.

A symbol of the third eye, the gem was once believed to balance yin/yang, protect against epilepsy and sunstroke, cure headaches and nose bleeds, and ensure a high yield in crops. Today, crystal healers believe that it can help men open their feminine emotional aspects. In some cultures, it is also believed to accentuate the wearer's nature, whether positive or negative.

MOONSTONE:	June's birthstone
Major Sources:	Brazil, Burma, India, Madagascar, Sri Lanka & Tanzania
Colors Found:	Colorless to brown, green, gray, pink, rainbow & yellow
Family:	Feldspar
Hardness:	6 to 6.5
Refractive Index:	1.51–1.53
Specific Gravity:	2.56–2.59

Just the facts

Moonstone is a potassium-rich orthoclase member of the feldspar group of minerals and is closely related to sunstone and labradorite. The name *feldspar* comes from the German *feldt spat*, meaning "field stone." This is because when feldspar weathers, it releases large amounts of plant nutrients like potassium, which enrich the soil.

Moonstone shows a blue whitish opalescence called *adularescence* (sometimes described as a billowy light or shimmer) that glides over its surface. Interference phenomena, due to the intergrowth of two different types of feldspar with different refractive indexes from the gem's layered structure, are the cause of this effect. Moonstones are often cut as cabochons to maximize it.

Traditionally, the gem has a silver to blue sheen, a transparent to translucent to opaque clarity, and a colorless body color. Sri Lankan rainbow moonstone, laboriously mined from a weathered pegmatite in Meetiyagoda, Sri Lanka, possesses all these qualities, and as it is quite rare and becoming rarer, it is definitely a "must have" for any jewelry collection. Interestingly, it typically displays such a stunning transparent clarity (not usually associated with this gemstone), intense bright blue shimmer, and dazzling iridescence (the rainbow-like color effect seen in some gems caused by cracks or structural layers breaking up light into spectral colors) that it can be cut as a faceted gemstone. This is truly unique and further accentuates the desirability of this highly collectible, exotic gemstone.

Tanzanian moonstone is a relatively new variety sourced from the Morogoro region of Tanzania.

Gray, white, and orange cabochon moonstone

Rainbow moonstone

MORGANITE

Morganite, or *pink beryl* as it was initially described, was discovered in Madagascar in 1911. It was Tiffany's celebrated gemologist, George Frederick Kunz, who renamed this unique gemstone in homage to the New York banker and his benefactor, John Pierpont Morgan.

Legends and lore
While morganite has had little time to generate myths and legends, all pink gemstones, aside from their obvious physical beauty, are believed by some to possess potent metaphysical properties connected with love and compassion.

Just the facts
Morganite, a member of the beryl family and sister gem to aquamarine and emerald, is colored by trace amounts of manganese that find their way into the beryl crystal structure. Typically found as flat, tabular crystals that resemble rose quartz, morganites are easily differentiated by their luster and brilliance.

When Mother Nature created morganite, she made the ideal gemstone to complement all complexions. Coming in pinks from subtle lavenders to hot fuchsias and even pastel pink apricot blends, the gem exudes charm and tenderness. Putting a unique twist on fashionable pink, it provides the perfect antidote to the stress of modern life.

Its durability, luster, clarity, brilliance, and myriad of beautiful pink hues make morganite immensely suitable as a jewelry gemstone, appropriate for everyday wear. The only factor impeding morganite's popularity is its scarcity.

MORGANITE:	Pink variety of beryl
Major Sources:	Afghanistan, Brazil, Madagascar, Namibia, Russia & USA
Colors Found:	Pink to salmon
Family:	Beryl: $Be_3Al_2Si_6O_{18}$
Hardness:	7.5 to 8
Refractive Index:	1.56–1.60; Uniaxial (−)
Specific Gravity:	2.66–2.87
Crystal System:	Hexagonal

Spinfire-cut morganite

Morganite and diamond ring
in yellow gold

Mixed-cut morganite

MOTHER OF PEARL

MOTHER OF PEARL

While Queen Elizabeth I gave *mother of pearl* its name in the 15th century, the beauty of it was used in the decoration of jewelry and ornaments 3,000 years before the birth of Christ. Also known as *nacre* (from the Arabic word for "shell," *naqqarah*), the name reflects the fact that these shells are the "mother" from which pearls are created.

Mother of pearl is the smooth lining of iridescent luster found in some mollusk shells such as oyster, abalone, mussel, and paua shells.

Legends and lore

In the 1920s, a series of tombs was excavated to the east of Babylon in the Middle East. The tombs were of Sumerian royalty from ancient Mesopotamia and yielded a treasure of gold, silver, gemstones, and several beautiful wooden ornaments and musical instruments inlaid with mother of pearl (a testament to the wealth and sophistication of this ancient culture). The silver lyre of Ur, found in one of the graves in the royal cemetery, dates to between 2600 and 2400 BC. The lyre was entirely covered in sheet silver and inlaid with mother of pearl.

In Asia, centuries before the birth of Christ, the Chinese learned that beads or tiny figures of deities slipped between the soft mantle and the shell of a living mollusk soon became coated with mother of pearl. These beads and carvings were then taken to temples and offered to the gods in the hope that they would bestow good luck.

The Yaqui Indians of Mexico, immortalized in the shamanic tales of Carlos Castaneda, wear a necklace called the *hopo'orosim*. The necklace is made of mother of pearl and is believed to provide the wearer with protection from evil.

By the 15th century, Europe's growing demand for mother of pearl for use in gold and silver rings, necklaces, and brooches had all but depleted its supplies in the Persian Gulf.

In 1568, the Solomon Islands, known as "the Pearl of the Pacific," were discovered by the Spanish explorer Alvaro de Mendana. On discovering the island's rich bounty of gold and mother of pearl, he gave the archipelago its current name, believing that he had found the mythical source of King Solomon's mines.

In Polynesian lore, the iridescence of mother of pearl is attributed to the spirits of coral and sand, Okana and Uaro, who, as legend has it, adorned Tahitian oysters in glistening cloaks covered in all the colors of the fish of the sea.

Just the facts

High-quality mother of pearl is produced by the members of the mollusk family called *bivalves* (two-part shells).

Mother of pearl's nacre forms when an organic particle becomes trapped within the mollusk or when the mollusk is injured in some way.

MOTHER OF PEARL:	Ancient gemstone
Major Sources:	China, Japan & South Pacific
Colors Found:	Various
Family:	Organic
Hardness:	2.5 to 4.5
Refractive Index:	1.52–1.66
Specific Gravity:	2.60–2.85

Sensing the object or damage, the living organism within the mollusk secretes calcium carbonate (in the form of aragonite) and the binding protein conchiolin. The layers of calcium carbonate settle and are interspersed by the conchiolin, which acts as a kind of organic glue binding the crystals together.

Mother of pearl is created by a living organism. Thus, environmental factors play a crucial role in its formation. As mother-of -pearl-producing mollusks cannot regulate their body temperatures, they are susceptible to changes in external conditions. Mother of pearl appears in a wide variety of colors, derived from its genetic make-up and the water in which it grows.

Carved mother of pearl cameo

Fancy-cut mother of pearl ring
in sterling silver

OBSIDIAN

This gem is supposedly named after Obsidian, a Roman said to have first brought this gem to Rome from Lake Shalla, Ethiopia.

Legends and lore

Obsidian is regarded as one of the most important "teachers" of the New Age movement. It is said to sharpen both external and internal vision. For some crystal healers, it is the warrior of truth and shows the self where the ego is and what we must change in order to advance to the next step of evolutionary growth.

Just the facts

Obsidian is formed by the rapid cooling of viscous lava due to volcanic explosions. Although it is made of the same minerals as granite, it cools so quickly that they do not have time to crystallize.

Obsidian has a glassy luster and is usually black or a very dark green. It can also be found in an almost-colorless form, though.

It may be fashioned into a razor-sharp cutting edge. Ancient civilizations used it for jewelry, mirrors, arrowheads, spearheads, scrapers, and cutting tools, such as the

OBSIDIAN:	Natural glass of volcanic origin
Major Sources:	Mexico & USA
Colors Found:	Almost clear, black & very dark green
Family:	Obsidian
Hardness:	5 to 5.5
Refractive Index:	1.45–1.55; SR
Specific Gravity:	2.35–2.60
Crystal System:	Amorphous

sacrificial knives of the Aztecs. Because of this, obsidian has been found in locations far from its original source. This might have confused a few gemologists, but it has helped us understand more about the travels of our ancestors.

Today, transparent specimens are faceted, usually into step cuts, while less transparent pieces are fashioned into cabochons.

Especially prized in jewelry, snowflake obsidian is a striking black, lustrous, opaque gem with bold white markings formed by internal bubbles or crystals of potassium feldspar, much like beautiful patterns of snowflakes on a black background.

Snowflake obsidian

ONYX

Onyx is a chalcedony quartz with a fine texture and parallel bands of alternate colors. Commonly known as *black magic*, this gem's name comes from the Greek word *onyx*, which means "fingernail" or "claw."

Legend says that one day while Venus was sleeping, Cupid cut her fingernails and left the clippings scattered on the ground. Because no part of a heavenly body can die, the gods turned them into a gem, which later became known as onyx.

Legends and lore

Related to its mythological origin, onyx is believed by some to encourage the growth of fingernails, hair, and skin. In Greek times, almost all colors of chalcedony quartz, from fingernail white to dark brown and black, were called onyx. Later, the Romans narrowed the term to refer to black and dark brown colors only. Today, when we think of onyx, we often preface the word with "black" to distinguish it from other varieties that come in white, reddish brown, green, brown, and banded colors. Onyx that is reddish brown and white is known as *sardonyx*.

ONYX:	Also known as Black Magic
Major Sources:	Brazil, India, Madagascar & Uruguay
Colors Found:	Black & white
Family:	Chalcedony Quartz: SiO_2
Hardness:	6.5 to 7
Refractive Index:	1.53–1.54
Specific Gravity:	2.60–2.64
Crystal System:	Trigonal (aggregate)

Onyx

With its consecutive layers of different colors, onyx was believed by the ancient Romans to be an excellent cameo gemstone (a gem carved in positive relief). Sardonyx was highly valued in Rome, especially for seals, because it was said never to stick to the wax. Roman General Publius Cornelius Scipio was known for wearing lots of sardonyx.

Onyx is often associated with instincts and intuition. It is believed to give one the power to deeply analyze a situation before reacting to it, as well as to provide better business acumen and management skills. Crystal healers also believe that it restores confidence in life and love, thereby increasing happiness.

Just the facts

Quartz gemstones are commonly separated into two groups based on the size of their individual crystals. The macrocrystalline quartz (large crystal) group includes many popular gemstones such as amethyst, ametrine, and citrine. Cryptocrystalline quartz includes species whose individual crystals are too small to be easily distinguished. Apart from being a variety within the group, chalcedony is also a catchall term to describe cryptocrystalline quartz and includes many gems that have been coveted since antiquity.

Fancy-cut faceted onyx ring
in sterling silver

OPAL

OPAL

Opal is one of the world's most coveted gemstones. Its name evolved from the Roman *opalus*, which was derived from the Greek *opallios*, meaning "to see a change of color." The Greek word was a modification of the ancient Indian Sanskrit name for opal, *upala*, which meant "precious stone." If one spoke in mixed tongues, then opal would be *opallios upala*, "to see a change of color precious stone."

While their body colors cover a broad spectrum, opals are most prized for their unique, fiery plays of color, reflecting and refracting light into flashes of multiple colors.

Legends and lore

Historically, opal was considered a lucky charm that brought beauty, success, and happiness to its wearer. The early Greeks believed opals embodied the powers of foresight and prophecy.

The Romans also cherished opals, considering them to be a symbol of hope and purity—an appropriate attribute for a gem with a rainbow locked within it.

The Arabs thought that opals must have fallen from heaven in flashes of lightning. According to Arab tradition, it is believed that the gems prevent lightning strikes, shield their wearers from any undesirable elements in their day-to-day lives, and give cloaks of invisibility to their wearers when desired.

Opal was featured in literature. Shakespeare referred to it in *Twelfth Night* as the "Queen of Gems."

History books would have us believe that the European supplies of opal came from India and the Middle East, but it is far more likely that they came from Hungarian mines.

Opal made headlines in the 1890s with the first samples of Australian opal. The Hungarians declared that the new Australian variety was not the real thing, as opals with such a fusion of fire and color had never been seen before. According to Koori (indigenous Australians) legend, the creator came down to earth on a rainbow to bring a message of peace to all humans. At the spot where his feet touched the ground, the stones became alive and started sparkling in all the colors of the rainbow, giving birth to Australian opals. Today, the gems are some of Australia's national treasures and some of the world's most prized gemstones.

Queen Victoria intervened in the near destruction of the 19th century opal market, when the writer Sir Walter Scott started a superstition that opals were bad luck for people not born in October. In one of his novels, the heroine owned an opal that burned fiery red when she was angry and turned ashen gray upon her death. Queen Victoria finally dispelled the curse by giving opal jewelry as gifts at a royal wedding.

Scandinavian women still wear opal hair bands to ward off the onset of gray hair. And some people believe that this gemstone has therapeutic properties that rejuvenate the inner spirit and invigorate the mind.

Just the facts

Opals possess flashes of rainbow colors that change with the angle of observation, called *play of color*. This effect is similar to the rainbow colors displayed on a soap bubble, only much more dramatic. This should not be confused with *opalescence*, which is the milky-blue or pearly appearance of opal caused by the scattering of light.

The physical structure of opal is unique. Tiny, precipitated spheres of silicon dioxide form a pyramid-shaped grid interspersed with water. Tiny, natural faults in this grid cause play of color.

Opals are typically classified depending on the *potch* (the host rock, also called the *matrix*) on which the opal is formed and their resulting transparency. For example, *black opal* has a black potch, *semi-black opal* has a potch darker than gray (but not quite black), *white opal* has a white potch, *Queensland boulder opal* has an ironstone (boulder) potch, and *jelly opal* (also known as *crystal opal*) is opal with no potch whatsoever. Distinguished from jelly opal by its minimal play of color, *fire opal* is jelly opal that displays extraordinary fiery yellows, tangerines, and reds. *Matrix opal* (also known as *opal with matrix*) is any opal where the potch, or matrix, is visible face up.

OPAL:	October's birthstone
Major Sources:	Australia, Brazil, Ethiopia, Mexico, Peru, South Africa, Tanzania, USA & Zimbabwe
Colors Found:	Various
Family:	Opal: $SiO_2 + H_2O$
Hardness:	5.5 to 6.5
Refractive Index:	1.37–1.52; SR
Specific Gravity:	1.98–2.50
Crystal System:	Amorphous

Opal actually exhibits many different colors, including cherry-colored specimens that rival ruby, fiery orange opals that sparkle like spessartine garnet, tropical blue gems as intense as chalcedony, and even gorgeous pinks and greens.

Today, approximately 95% of the world's opal is sourced from a handful of prominent mining areas in Australia, namely Lightning Ridge, Coober Pedy, Andamooka, and Mintabie.

Black opal

Black opal is principally found at Lightning Ridge in New South Wales, Australia. Known as the "King of Opals," Lightning Ridge black opal has been coveted since it was discovered in 1902. Located 575 miles north of Sydney, Lightning Ridge (a free-wheeling town of about 15,000 people) is the world's major source of the finest black opal.

This magnificent gemstone is the most coveted form of opal. Its dark background color sets the spectral colors ablaze, much like a storm cloud behind a rainbow. The black background provides contrast and intensity to this opal's play of color. So prized is black opal that even wafer-thin slices are made into doublets or triplets to give them enough strength and depth to set into gold rings and other jewelry items.

The black opal mining fields of Lightning Ridge and the majority of Australia's opal fields are located in a geological phenomenon called *the Great Australian Basin*. The basin was formed

From left to right: Lightning Ridge black opal, Queensland boulder opal, Mexican fire opal, and Brazilian fire opal

from sediments of a large inland sea that existed over 140 million years ago. Approximately 120 million years later, sandstones were deposited by waterways over the top of these sedimentary rocks. Eventually, these younger rocks weathered, and their silica filtered down to cavities in the older host rock in the form of a gel. The silica gel hardened, forming around a nucleus, creating the opal's characteristic regular spheres and voids. It's the diffraction of light through these transparent spaces that produces opal's brilliant play of colors.

Opals are mined directly from narrow seams in sedimentary rock, and the mining involves hard digging with picks and shovels 20–60 feet underground. Buckets are then loaded and hauled to the surface using simple mechanical winches. The rough opal (called *nobbies*) is initially separated by hand prior to sieving. The remaining opal nobbies are then taken to small, converted cement mixers to wash off the excess dirt.

Unfortunately, all Australian opals (especially those from Lightning Ridge) are becoming increasingly scarce. The old fields at Lightning Ridge that produced high-dome cabochons are virtually depleted, with only marginal areas presently being worked. Despite the fact that the government has opened many new prospective areas, to date, there have been no significant new prospects found. Opal production at Lightning Ridge is half of what it was ten years ago. The current supply problems are infuriating as international demand remains high. The present jewelry trends favoring color have seen an increase in opal use among the world's leading jewelry houses.

Boulder opal

Boulder opal is found sparsely distributed over a wide area of Australian ironstone or boulder country where the opal (silica mix) fills veins, cracks, cavities, and crevices in ironstone boulders. Opal-bearing boulder is always cut to include the host brown ironstone. The GIA (Gemological Institute of America) classifies two types: gems with ironstone visible face up, called *opal with matrix*, and gems with no visible inclusions, called *opal in matrix*. Boulder opal is usually cut as opal with matrix to the contours of the opal vein, creating a baroque, wavy surface often freeform and irregular in shape, making each boulder opal unique. Located northwest of Lightning Ridge, in western Queensland, the Queensland boulder opal fields encompass a vast area centered on the town of Quilpie and extending as far north as Winton and south to Cunamulla. Recent years have seen slightly lower production levels, with any fine gems quickly snapped up.

From left to right: green opal, Mintabie jelly opal, and two different hues of Mexican jelly opal

Known for its lively, flaming, bright rich colors, this variety is in very high demand and extremely popular. Interest in Queensland boulder opal has increased markedly over the last 20 years as this unique type of opal gains recognition from gem enthusiasts the world over.

Ethiopian opal

If you love the beauty and richness of Brazilian and Australian solid opal, then Ethiopian opal should captivate your heart and mind. Discovered initially at Yita Ridge in the Shewa province of Ethiopia, small amounts of rough started trickling out in the mid-1990s, giving a hint of the incredible potential in this remote portion of the world. A subsequent discovery in 2008 found another source of opal near the Welo district. This new find offered beautiful, stable, solid opal with exceptional play of color. Gem-quality stones cut from this rough rivaled the beauty and majesty of fine Australian material, but they became more readily available and affordable.

Unlike its Australian counterpart, Ethiopian opal is volcanic in origin rather than sedimentary. Volcanic opal is known as *hydrophane*. The term comes from two Greek roots meaning "water loving." Most Welo opal will absorb water readily and change from opaque to translucent—or even transparent—depending on the source of the rough. In some cases, this transformation highlights the opal's play of color, and this is a major point of interest for many gem collectors.

The impact of this discovery is so great that many sources refer to Ethiopia as the *New Australia*. With this amazing find, the *Queen of Gems* is once again in the limelight of the gemstone kingdom.

Fire opal

Fire opal is appropriately named for its fiery cherries, sunburst yellows, and deep tangerines. Unique and mysterious, it is remarkable because unlike many other opals, its play of color is minimal. Also known as *Mexican opal, Mexican fire opal, Tanzanian fire opal, cherry fire opal, Ethiopian fire opal, Brazilian fire opal,* or *sun opal*, its legendary popularity instead comes from its breathtaking brilliance, opalescence, extraordinarily fiery hues, and stunning clarity. Fire opals have been treasured in the Americas since the time of the Aztecs, when they were named *quetzalitzlipyollitli* or "gem of the bird of paradise." Coveted by the Aztecs as symbols of intense love, such radiant gemstones were believed to have emerged from the primordial waters of creation. While fire opal is predominately sourced from Mexico (and occasionally Australia), this gem has recently been found in Tanzania, Ethiopia, Mali, and now Brazil. While opal has been mined in Brazil since approximately 1945, production has always been very limited, making it difficult to secure commercial quantities. Today, the Piaui State is increasingly garnering

From left to right: Mexican jelly opal, two examples of Mexican matrix opal, and Andamooka semi-black opal

international acclaim for its opals, with their quality favorably compared to Australian opals, which are arguably the world's finest. With the enforcement of new mining regulations, scarcity has increased, strengthening the appeal of this relatively new addition to the opal family.

Green opal

Discovered in the 1960s, *green opal* is a green translucent gem that resembles chrysoprase or jade and is commonly called *prase opal* or *chrysopal* because of its resemblance to chrysoprase. It is mined in the Arusha region of Tanzania (the same region as tanzanite). While this gem does not display the play of color found in some opals, its mint to apple-green body color has made it very popular for jewelry. Trace amounts of nickel give this opal its unique color.

Jelly opal

Jelly opal (also known as *water opal* or *crystal opal*) is mined in Mexico and Australia. Offering an attractive blend of indistinct colors, it is a transparent, pure opal with a gelatinous appearance and an occasionally pronounced opalescence (bluish sheen). The play of color is a subtle sheen dancing throughout the gem, rather than distinct color potches. When held out in direct light, jelly opal can display some of the most intense opal colors. Very occasionally, it is also found in Lightning Ridge, Australia, where it is essentially black opal without the black potch background. This is the type of opal used in opal inlay jewelry that has the base of the setting blackened (typically using black rhodium) before a precisely cut crystal opal is set within.

Peruvian opal

Hailing from the Andes and coveted by the ancient Incas, *Peruvian opal* is extremely rare and exhibits an exquisite translucent coloring. While it typically comes in blue or pink colors, greens are also occasionally found.

Semi-black opal

With a brighter transparency than black opal, *semi-black opal* has a body color darker than gray, but not quite black. Opacity is the key that divides black from semi-black, with black opal appearing more opaque than the other. Semi-black opal was discovered at Andamooka in the 1930s. Situated 398 miles north by road from Adelaide, South Australia, Andamooka remains a typical dusty "wild west" desert town. In the 1960s, when Andamooka was booming, an opal setting (that was worth hundreds of thousands of dollars at the time) was presented to Queen Elizabeth II.

While Andamooka opals remain world renowned, only a small amount of opal is now mined from there, due to high logistical expenses related to its remoteness. Andamooka opal is typically exceptionally high quality, but it has become more difficult to source in the last few years. Andamooka is reportedly very quiet at present—with less than 50 serious miners.

White opal

White opal is translucent with a creamy appearance that dominates the diffracted colors. While all of the Australian opal fields produce white opal, the majority is mined in Coober Pedy.

Commenting that "there is in them a softer fire than the ruby, there is the brilliant purple of the amethyst, and the sea green of the emerald—all shining together in incredible union," opal clearly impressed Pliny the Elder (23–79 AD), Roman historian and author of the *Historia Naturalis*, the world's first encyclopedia. With only 25% of mined opal finding its way into jewelry, if you're looking to be impressed with the gem, there is no better place to start building your opal collection than at JTV.

PEARL

Pearls are some of the oldest known gems and, for centuries, were considered the most valuable—so valuable, in fact, that the Roman General Vitellius allegedly financed an entire military campaign with just one of his mother's pearl earrings.

Thankfully, the days of island inhabitants free diving into azure oceans to harvest pearls are more or less over. The lust for uncultured pearls once decimated entire species of mollusks, relegating this gem of the sea to the elite few. Today, thanks to the innovations of Japanese noodle maker, Kokichi Mikimoto (the man who perfected pearl farming and who convinced the world to accept them), these fragile ecosystems are now safe, with natural uncultured pearls usually appearing only as antiques.

Legends and lore

The Romans were particularly enamored of this gem of the sea. Rome's pearl craze reached its zenith during the 1st century BC, when upper-class Roman women wore their pearls to bed so they could be reminded of their wealth immediately upon awakening. (The lower ranks were forbidden from wearing them.) They also sewed so many into their gowns that they actually walked on their pearl-encrusted hems. The famously excessive Emperor Caligula, having made his beloved horse a consul, decorated it with a pearl necklace.

A lover of luxury, Julius Caesar, apart from his well-known military accomplishments, was also an expert in pearls and could reportedly accurately ascertain their value by simply weighing them in his hand.

Cleopatra flaunted her enormous wealth and power during a competition with Marc Anthony to see who could host the most lavish dinner party. She allegedly crushed a pearl from one of her earrings into a glass of wine to demonstrate to Marc Anthony how she could drink the wealth of nations.

The first known source of pearls was the Persian Gulf, and the ancients of the area believed that the gems were a symbol of the moon and had magical powers. Indeed, the oldest known pearl jewelry is a necklace found in the sarcophagus of a Persian princess who died in 520 BC.

The earliest written record of their value is in the *Shu King*, a 23 BC Chinese book in which the scribe sniffs that a lesser king sent tribute of "strings of pearls not quite round." The Chinese also used pearls in medicinal ways to cure eye ailments, heart trouble, indigestion, fever, and bleeding. To this day, pearl powder is still popular in China as a skin whitener and cosmetic.

In India, pearls were believed to give peace of mind and strengthen the body and soul.

In antiquity, it was thought that swallowing whole or powdered pearls cured matters of the mind and heart, strengthened nerves, and even improved virility.

The Koran states that a good Muslim, upon entering the Kingdom of Heaven, "is crowned with pearls of incomparable luster, and is attended by beautiful maidens resembling hidden pearls."

While Queen Isabella had to hock her impressive collection of jewelry to fund Christopher Columbus' expedition to discover the New World, the investment paid off, as the discovery of pearls in Central American waters added to the wealth of Spain. The flood of American pearls onto the European market earned the newly discovered continent the nickname "Land of Pearls." Unfortunately, greed and lust for these gems of the sea resulted in the depletion of virtually all the American pearl oyster populations by the 17th century.

During the Dark Ages, while fair maidens of nobility cherished delicate pearl necklaces, gallant knights often wore pearls onto the battlefield. They believed that the magic possessed by the lustrous gems would protect them from harm.

Pearls have long been considered ideal wedding gifts because they symbolize purity and innocence. In the Hindu religion, the presentation of an undrilled pearl and its piercing has formed part of the marriage ceremony. In the West, pearls are the recommended gift for couples celebrating their 3rd and 30th wedding anniversaries.

Just the facts

The pearl begins life as a foreign body (generally a parasite), which makes its way into the shell of a marine or freshwater mollusk—usually oysters or clams. The mollusk's defense mechanism starts to coat the intruder with layers of a slightly iridescent substance, "nacre" (from the Arabic word for "shell," *naqqarah*), which is the attractive outside of the pearl. In its natural environment, this will, after many years, form a pearl that is of a significant size and quality.

Unlike natural pearls, cultivated pearls do not begin as accidental intruders. First cultivated by the Chinese as early as the 12th century, the

PEARL:	June's birthstone
Major Sources:	Australia, Burma, China, Indonesia, Japan, Philippines, Tahiti & Vietnam
Colors Found:	Black, cream, gold, golden yellow, gray, orange, pink, silver & white
Family:	Organic
Hardness:	2.5 to 4.5
Refractive Index:	1.52–1.66
Specific Gravity:	2.60–2.85

process starts with *nucleation*. A cultivated pearl usually begins its life when a spherical bead or a piece of mantle tissue is placed inside the mollusk. After this seeding process, the pearl farmers place the mollusks in wire-mesh baskets and suspend them in water. The aquaculturists carefully tend to the mollusks, overseeing their development for 18 months to five years. The depth of the nacre coating, an important factor in determining the color of pearls, depends on how long the seeded pearls are left in place before being harvested. Usually, only half of the pearls will be marketable, and less than 10% of these will be top quality. While pearls are classified as colored gems, there is a unique appeal about them. Unlike other gemstones that are born of earth and fire, pearls are waterborn organic gems that originate from living animals. They are also unique in the sense that the principles of the 4 C's (color, cut, clarity, and carat weight) cannot be applied to them. The evaluation of pearls requires a different set of criteria. A pearl is appraised according to the display of color, luster, surface clarity, shape, and size.

Pearl's two colors

The body colors themselves can be white, cream, pink, rose, golden, silver, gray, and black. As color preference is subjective, there is no such thing as a bad body color—it is purely a matter of choice. Apart from the obvious body color, there is actually a second color to consider when evaluating pearls. It is a result of subtle iridescence. While not instantly obvious, especially when similar to the body color, this effect lends pearls much of their allure. Typically, this iridescence is seen most strongly on the crest of a pearl's horizon. This beautiful, shimmering effect is known as the "orient," or overtone, and denotes the depth of the nacre. Pearls with rich colorful orients are generally more coveted than those that have little or no orient.

Pearl luster

Pearls are bright, reflective gemstones. While these with clean and even surfaces reflect more light than those with blemished surfaces, please remember that as a natural creation, like inclusions in mineral gems, most pearls do have blemishes.

Intelligent jewelers solve this problem by concealing blemishes near the drill holes.

Weight and size

As with other gemstones, value and size are intrinsically linked. The bigger the pearl, the more desirable it becomes. However, there is one important difference: pearls are measured and expressed by their size, not weight (e.g., 8.5 millimeters).

Pearl locations

As with all things natural, pearls can only grow in the right conditions. Different pearl varieties from different locations command different prices. The best-quality pearls are found in the waters of French Polynesia, Japan, and China. However, due to the different environments, mollusk species, and farming techniques, all cultivated pearls have their own distinctive qualities.

Freshwater pearl

Freshwater pearl bracelets

Freshwater pearls

Although historically originating in Japan, China is now a major producer of freshwater pearls. Our Chinese freshwater pearls are farmed in the Fuchum, Wu, and Ling rivers of the Zhejiang province in southern China. The country has successfully concentrated on freshwater pearls, using not oysters but freshwater clams. The humble clam, while not as widely celebrated as its cousin, the oyster, is equally capable of producing high-quality pearls.

Tahitian pearls

Tahitian pearls are from French Polynesia and are named after the tropical island of Tahiti. Grown in the large, black-lipped saltwater oyster (*pinctada margaritifera*), Tahitian pearls are celebrated for their exceptional beauty.

Tahiti's pure and tranquil waters are the ideal cultivation grounds for the dramatic Tahitian pearl.

Tahitian legend says that Te Ufi (*pinctada margaritifera*) was given to man by Oro, the god of peace and fertility, who came to earth on a rainbow and offered the pearl to the beautiful princess Bora Bora as a sign of eternal love.

Tahitian pearl

First appearing in Europe in 1845, Napoleon III's wife, Empress Eugenie, was responsible for bringing Tahitian pearls into fashion. After the fall of Napoleon, Empress Eugenie's necklace was auctioned at Christie's for $20,000. *Ezra* was the most famous natural Tahitian pearl, the centerpiece of a necklace that was part of the Russian crown jewels.

Tahitian black pearls are prized and admired throughout the world. The first pearl farms were established on the atoll of Hikueru and the island of Bora Bora in the early 1960s. Exports began in 1972, and production was subsequently expanded on the islands of Marutea Sud and Mangareva. Today, Tahitian black pearls are cultivated in pearl farms in a sprawling group of atolls and islands in French Polynesia, primarily the lagoons of the Tuamotu-Gambier Archipelago.

Tahitian pearls generally range in size from 8–16 millimeters and consist of many thousands of layers of aragonite (a variety of calcium carbonate). In contrast to many other pearl varieties, Tahitian pearls are cultured for 4–5 years and have a nacre thickness of 3–10 millimeters.

Tahitian pearls display a shimmering orient, or overtone, that is green, blue, pink, or violet in color. These orient colors are in striking contrast to their silver to black body color and are sometimes given specific names (e.g., deep green is called *fly wing; peacock* is used for the combination of green and pink; *eggplant* is a dark-toned body color combined with pink).

South Sea pearls

Highly coveted, South Sea pearls come from Australia, Indonesia, and the Philippines. Cultured in varieties of *pinctada maxima*, these large, warm-water-loving, gold- and silver-lipped oysters produce pearls of fabulous colors.

Cultured golden South Sea pearls

Cultured Tahitian pearl and diamond ring in white gold

PERIDOT

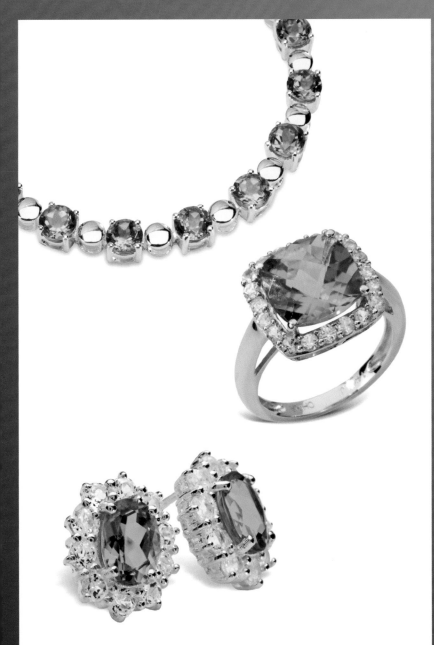

PERIDOT

Shining with a bright green glow even at night, *peridot* was called the "gem of the sun" by the ancient Egyptians and the "evening emerald" by Romans. It was a favorite gemstone of Cleopatra and was historically mistaken for emerald. The pronunciation of this popular gem is often confused and should be pronounced *pair-ee-doh,* as opposed to *pair-ee-dot.*

Peridot's name origin is uncertain, but several theories exist. Some sources speculate that it comes from the 13th century Middle English word *peridote,* meaning "bright spot" or "bright button," an apt description for this gem, given its brilliance. Other sources attribute it to the French *peritot,* meaning "unclear," probably due to its silky appearance. While some sources suggest the word peridot comes from the Greek *peridona,* indicating "plentiful," this seems unlikely because this gem was scarce even in classical times. Given the ancient source of peridot, the most likely candidate is the Arabic word *faridat,* which simply means "gem."

Legends and lore
Popular in early Greek and Roman jewelry, peridot has been coveted since 1500 BC, when the Egyptians started mining it on Zeberget Island, later known as St. John's Island, about 50 miles off the Egyptian coast in the Red Sea. Interestingly, *zabargad* is the Arabic word for peridot.

Peridot mining was traditionally done at night, when the gem's natural glow made it easier to spot. The ancient Egyptians even believed that peridot became invisible under the sun's rays. They also believed that the gem was colored by the golden glow of their sun god, Ra, and was, thus, a powerful protector from harm.

Hawaiians believe peridot is the goddess Pele's tears, while it is mentioned in the Bible (using its old name *chrysolite,* meaning "golden stone" in Greek) as being one of the "stones of fire" (Ezekiel 28:13–16) that was given to Moses and set in the breastplate of Aaron (Exodus 28:15–30). Peridot is also one of the 12 gemstones set in the foundations of the city walls of Jerusalem (Revelations 21:19) and associated with the Apostle Bartholomew.

Peridot

While Cleopatra reportedly had a fine collection of "emerald" jewelry, it was, in reality, predominantly peridot.

The Ottoman sultans gathered the largest collection of peridot during their 600-year reign, from 1300–1918, with an impressive array of loose gemstones as well as earrings, rings, and other jewelry.

Powdered peridot has been used to cure asthma, and a peridot placed under the tongue of someone in the grip of a fever was believed to lessen his or her thirst. Legend has it that drinking from a peridot goblet can increase the potency of medicines.

Pirates believed peridot had the power to drive away evil spirits (and the night's terrors), especially if set in gold. But for protection from evil spirits, they believed it had to be pierced, strung on donkey hair, and worn on the left arm.

Possibly the most unusual peridot comes from meteorites and is called *pallasites*, after their 1772 discoverer, a German scientist called Peter Simon Pallas. Some of these stones have even been faceted and set in jewelry—one of the few extraterrestrial gemstones known to man. In 2003, peridot was discovered on Mars, making it the first gemstone to be discovered on another planet.

PERIDOT:	August's birthstone
Major Sources:	Burma, China, Kenya, Pakistan, South Africa, Tanzania, USA & Vietnam
Colors Found:	Green to yellowish green
Family:	Olivine: $(Mg_2Fe_2)SiO_4$
Hardness:	6.5 to 7
Refractive Index:	1.65–1.70; Biaxial (+ or −)
Specific Gravity:	3.28–3.48
Crystal System:	Orthorhombic

Just the facts

Peridot is the gem variety of olivine and exhibits colors ranging from golden lime greens to rich grass greens. Traditionally, the most coveted color hues have been the rich grass greens. However, many peridots with slight yellowish hues still exhibit attractive colors that are extremely popular. This once again demonstrates that your individual preference should always be the primary factor when collecting colored gemstones.

Gems that owe their color to basic elements in their chemical formulas are termed *idiochromatic,* or "self-colored," and *allochromatic,* or "other colored," if they are colorless when pure. In the case of peridot, the coloring agent is iron. Since iron is part of the gem's formula, it always has some color (green to yellowish green).

Because of the way peridot splits and bends light, it has an attractive, velvety, silky appearance with a shining rich glow.

While the San Carlos Apache Reservation in Arizona has the world's largest gem-quality peridot deposit, China has recently become a major producer. In 1994, an exciting new deposit was discovered in Pakistan, producing some of the finest peridot ever seen. The new mine is located 15,000 feet above sea level in the Nanga Parbat region in the far west of the Himalayan mountains in the Pakistani part of Kashmir.

Some of the world's finest peridots come from Pyaung Gaung, in the northern part of Burma's Mogok Stone Tract. Faceted stones of 100–200 carats or more are known from this deposit, which also produces the occasional cat's-eye and star peridot.

Emerald-cut peridot

PEZZOTTAITE

Displaying gorgeous, deep raspberry pinks, *pezzottaite* is a relatively new gemstone that has been subject to much confusion due to its similarities with red emerald (bixbite).

Just the Facts

Pezzottaite was discovered in November 2002 at the Sakavalana mine, located about 87 miles southwest of Antsirabe in southern Madagascar. The initial deposit yielded some extremely rare, large crystals, and it is now practically depleted (although small amounts are now mined elsewhere in Madagascar). The Sakavalana pegmatite where pezzottaite was discovered was mined by the French for tourmaline during the 1940s. The initial pezzottaite deposit was discovered in a large crystal-bearing cavity that also contained tourmaline and spodumene. Not surprisingly, pezzottaite was initially mistakenly sold as tourmaline in Madagascar.

PEZZOTTAITE:	Initially confused with beryl
Major Sources:	Madagascar
Colors Found:	Pink to raspberry
Family:	Pezzottaite: $Cs(Be_2Li)Al_2Si_6O_{18}$
Hardness:	7.5 to 8
Refractive Index:	1.60–1.62; Uniaxial (–)
Specific Gravity:	3.04–3.14
Crystal System:	Trigonal

Pezzottaite is mined from granitic pegmatites using hand tools, making its extraction slow and difficult.

Having a slightly different chemical composition to red emerald ($Be_3Al_2Si_6O_{18}$), it was named *pezzottaite* ($Cs[Be_2Li]Al_2Si_6O_{18}$) in September 2003, after Dr. Federico Pezzotta of the Museo Civico di Storia Naturale, Milan, Italy, in recognition of his contributions to the mineralogy of Madagascar.

Pezzottaite has a variety of trade names, including *Madagascan raspberyl, raspberyl* and *raspberry beryl*. While it is closely related to the beryl family and is visually similar, it is, in fact, a unique species, making its trade names somewhat misleading.

As they are in emeralds, inclusions in pezzottaite are common, especially in the larger carat weights. However, pezzottaite's rarity and novelty for gemstone collectors have always been its primary factors. Pezzottaite has all the attributes a gem needs—beauty, durability, and rarity. Far scarcer than ruby, this rare gem truly is a unique fashion statement.

Pezzottaite

PREHNITE

With its gorgeous greens and unique translucency, *prehnite* is a wonderful, rare, exotic gem, which, despite a suitable durability, has only recently gained popularity as a jewelry gemstone.

Named after Dutch mineralogist and early governor of the "Cape of Good Hope" colony, Colonel Hendrik von Prehn (1733–1785), who discovered it in the Cradock district of the eastern Cape province, South Africa, in the early 18th century, prehnite was the first mineral to be named after a person.

Legend and lore

Known as the "prediction stone" among spiritual healers, it is believed that prehnite can enhance one's dreaming and remembrance. Some crystal healers also believe that prehnite's color and unusual touch are ideal for stress release.

Just the facts

Prehnite's bright, almost luminescent, swirling green colors (reminiscent of jade), mesmerizing clarity, and striking luster make it an extremely attractive collector's gem.

PREHNITE:	Also known as the "Prediction Stone"
Major Sources:	Australia
Colors Found:	Colorless, green, gray, white & yellow
Family:	Prehnite: $Ca_2Al_2Si_3O_{10}(OH)_2$ + Fe
Hardness:	6 to 6.5
Refractive Index:	1.61–1.67: Biaxial (+)
Specific Gravity:	2.82–2.94
Crystal System:	Orthorhombic (aggregate)

In his book, *Gemstones of the World*, Walter Schumann describes prehnite as a transparent to translucent gemstone, which accounts for its "cloudy" appearance. This is totally normal, and like many gemstones, its distinctive appearance is key to its appeal. While its main colors are a range of pleasant greens that are often unique to prehnite, yellow, gray, colorless, and white varieties also exist. Prehnite has some interesting common names, including *grape jade* (in China, it is called *putao yü*, meaning "grape jade," due to crystal formations that look like a bunch of grapes), *cape emerald* (for the location of its discovery and visual similarities to emeralds), and *prediction stone* (see above).

Prehnite is usually found in cavities along fractures of basalt. The Australian deposits occur in scattered outcrops of Antrim Plateau Volcanics of early Cambrian age (about 570 million years old) and consist of massive basalt up to 197 feet thick. Although the primary Australian deposits cover thousands of square miles in the east Kimberley (Western Australia) and the adjoining Northern Territory, gem-quality prehnite is very scarce. Most of the prehnite you'll see on JTV hails from Australia, which has about 90% of the world's reserves of this beautiful green gem.

Prehnite pendant in yellow gold   Prehnite

PYRITE & MARCASITE

PYRITE & MARCASITE

Pyrite has a shiny golden yellow color and a metallic luster. The name comes from the Greek word *pyr*, meaning "a gemstone that strikes fire." This is due to the sparks produced when pyrite strikes iron. While pyrite is often mistaken for gold, the two are differentiated by pyrite's lighter, tougher, broken-faced grains. As only a fool would mistake it for gold, pyrite is also known as *fool's gold*.

Marcasite is often used as a jewelry trade name for pyrite. Although it is called marcasite, it is actually pyrite, as true marcasite is unsuitable for jewelry. The confusion between the two dates back several hundred years, due to their similar appearance. Marcasite's name was derived from *marqashith*, the Arabic word for "pyrite," after an old province in northeastern Persia (Iran). Marcasite jewelry (pyrite) is a popular style that became fashionable during Queen Victoria's reign. The jewelry normally uses pyrite cut and is polished in a circular outline (square-cut gems are occasionally used) and pavé set between sterling silver beads to enhance their brilliance. They were originally used because they catch the light and glow like small diamonds. Today, marcasite jewelry is often fashioned into .925 sterling silver rings, earrings, pendants, brooches, necklaces, and bracelets.

Legends and lore

Used by the ancient Greeks in pins, earrings, and amulets, pyrite was once polished by Native Americans and used as mirrors. It is also known as "healer's gold" and is highly regarded by crystal healers as a gemstone of intellect and protection.

Just the facts

Pyrite is composed of iron sulfide. When found in its raw state, pyrite crystals can be shaped as cubes, octahedrons, and pyritohedrons (12 faces). Twinning causes "iron crosses" that look like interpenetrating cubes. Collectors particularly favor a flattened nodular variety called *pyrite suns* or *pyrite dollars*.

Pyrite is present in igneous rocks (as an accessory mineral), in sedimentary rocks (especially black shale), and in metamorphic rocks (most notably in slates). It is sometimes found as a replacement mineral in fossils.

PYRITE:	Called *marcasite* in the jewelry trade
Major Sources:	Austria, China, Mexico, Romania, Russia, South Africa & Spain
Colors Found:	Golden yellow
Family:	Pyrite: FeS_2
Hardness:	6 to 6.5
Refractive Index:	Completely opaque
Specific Gravity:	5.00–5.20
Crystal System:	Cubic

Faceted pyrite

QUARTZ

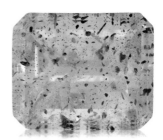

QUARTZ

The Greeks originally named quartz *krystallos*, meaning "ice," but this term was soon applied to any crystal. In fact, the modern name of quartz is derived from the Saxon word *querklufterz*, meaning "cross-vein-ore."

Although quartz of sufficient beauty to be set into jewelry is not available in great abundance, it is found in many geological environments and is a component of almost every rock type. It is also the most varied in terms of varieties, colors, and forms. The gem varieties of quartz have been used as gemstones for thousands of years.

Legends and lore

The ancients of India considered quartz to have special properties as transformers, as well as keepers, of energy. To this day, its crystals are used universally in meditation, as they are believed to possess healing properties and other diverse metaphysical powers.

Folklorists classify quartz as a receptive gemstone credited with the ability to attract positive energies such as peace and love. The subtle energy of quartz is said to balance the emotions, giving inner peace, harmony, and enhancing the bonds of relationships. It is also said to calm aggression and increase self-esteem.

Just the facts

Quartz gemstones are commonly separated into two groups based on the size of their individual crystals.

The macrocrystalline quartz (large crystal) group includes many popular gemstones such as amethyst, ametrine, citrine, green amethyst (prasiolite), rose quartz, rutilated quartz, smoky quartz, and tiger's eye.

QUARTZ:	Ancient gemstone
Major Sources:	Australia, Bolivia, Brazil, India, Kenya, Madagascar, Mozambique, Mexico, Russia, South Africa, Tanzania, Uruguay & Zambia
Colors Found:	Various
Family:	Quartz: SiO_2
Hardness:	6.5 to 7
Refractive Index:	1.53–1.55; Uniaxial (+)
Specific Gravity:	2.58–2.91
Crystal System:	Trigonal

Cryptocrystalline quartz includes varieties whose individual crystals are too small to be easily distinguished. Apart from being a variety within the group, chalcedony is also a catchall term to describe cryptocrystalline quartz and includes many gems that have been coveted since antiquity, such as agate, carnelian, sard, chrysoprase, bloodstone, and jasper.

Phenomena sometimes observed in quartz include asterism (star effect) and chatoyancy (cat's-eye effect).

Amethyst is the queen of the quartz varieties, and in better qualities, it is among the most coveted of quartzes.

Ametrine is a bi-color variety that is part amethyst colored and part citrine colored.

Blue moon quartz is also called *dumortierite quartz* or, sometimes, just *dumortierite*. It is an opaque to translucent blue variety, owing its color to microscopic inclusions of fibrous magnesioriebeckite or crocidolite. Blue moon quartz is from one of the old mines of southern Brazil in a region called Uruguaiana in the Rio Grande do Sul state. The "blue moon" prefix is self-explanatory: the gem looks like a full moon shimmering on a clear night. For crystal healers, blue moon quartz is a gem that can enhance organizational abilities, self-discipline, and orderliness.

Citrine is a yellow variety of quartz that takes its name from *citron*, the French word for "lemon."

Phantom quartz (also known as *ghost crystals, specter crystals,* or *shadow crystals*) is an unusual gemstone that exhibits a phenomenon called a *phantom*. Phantoms can sometimes be seen in the interior of quartz crystals as a permanent record of earlier stages in the crystal's formation, much like growth rings in a tree.

Green amethyst (*prasiolite*) is a confusing gem because it is traded under a variety of names and can easily be mistaken for other gem types.

Rainbow quartz (including *lavender quartz, neptune quartz, fuchsia quartz,* and *coral quartz*) is visually similar to mystic topaz and is produced using the same physical vapor deposition (PVD) coating process. Applied to top-quality natural white quartz, the treatment is permanent with normal wear.

Smoky quartz is an earth-toned, transparent quartz that comes in a variety of shades, including cognac. Also known as *champagne on ice,* smoky quartz gets its rich, warm colors from color centers related to aluminum. A variety of smoky quartz is *cairngorm,* which owes its name to the legendary source in the Scottish Highlands. Smoky quartz is the national gem of Scotland, whose national scepter includes a large smoky quartz.

Rock crystal (also known as *white quartz*) is colorless quartz.

Rose quartz is the pink variety of quartz. Rarely transparent, facet-grade gems will usually display a beautiful misty appearance.

Rutilated quartz (also known as *rutilite, golden rutile quartz, venus' hair stone,* or *cupid's darts*) is a beautiful gemstone produced by large inclusions of golden rutile needles in clear colorless quartz.

Tiger's eye is a type of quartz where the asbestos mineral, crocidolite, is replaced by quartz, keeping the fibrous structure. It is typically a golden or copper color. Bluish tiger's eye is termed *hawk's eye.*

Star quartz is a fascinating gem that clearly displays asterism (the star effect) and is colorless, blue, pink, or silver. The stars can contain six or more rays and roll around the gem as it is moved. In some cases, the star is seen in transmitted light, a phenomenon termed *diasterism.*

From left to right: golden rutile quartz, rose quartz, smoky quartz, and blue moon quartz

RHODOCHROSITE

One of nature's more exotic treasures, rhodochrosite is a true collector's find. Highly prized for its striking rose-red color, well-formed rhombohedral crystals are extremely difficult to obtain and are rarely sacrificed to the lapidary's wheel. Fine-quality gems are scarce—and custom-made jewelry pieces even more so. Although special care is required, rhodochrosite gemstones make stunning additions to any style of jewelry.

Just the facts

Rhodochrosite is a carbonate mineral belonging to the calcite group. Its name is derived from two Greek roots meaning "rose" and "color," allusions to its reddish variety. Semitranslucent to opaque material is often carved for decorative purposes or cabbed for use in jewelry. This material often exhibits a series of stripes or bands of various shades, which form a "bacon strip" or "bull's eye" pattern. Finer material is rarely set in jewelry due to its softer nature and sensitivity to pressure. Sensitivity to pressure is a function of perfect cleavage in three directions.

Color ranges from pink to red, often with an orange component. Yellowish to brownish material also exists. Sources of fine-quality rhodochrosite include Argentina, Peru, South Africa, and the United States (Colorado).

RHODOCHROSITE:	Very rarely transparent
Major Sources:	Argentina, Chile, Mexico, Peru, South Africa & USA
Colors Found:	Pink, pink-orange & red
Family:	Rhodochrosite
Hardness:	4.0
Refractive Index:	1.608–1.617
Specific Gravity:	3.04–3.14
Crystal System:	Trigonal

Sweet Home Mine
rhodochrosite

Free-form rhodochrosite
bacon strip pattern

RHODONITE

Another mineral that falls into the category of rare and exotic is fine-quality *rhodonite*, highly prized by collectors of specimens and gemstones. Its name, derived from two Greek roots, means "rose-colored stone."

Just the facts

Rhodonite is rarely seen as transparent crystals. It is commonly found in massive or granular forms, which are carved into decorative pieces or cabbed for use in jewelry. Color ranges from pink to red or brownish red, often with blackish veins throughout.

Traditionally, fine, gem-quality rough has been rare, but a find in Brazil yielded some exceptionally clean, vibrant reddish rough capable of producing transparent gems in excess of five carats. (Prior to 2007, most gem-quality stones were less than two carats in size.) Another amazing aspect was the discovery of a small percentage of rough that yielded cat's eyes, an optical phenomenon that was new to this gemstone. Care must be taken when cutting rhodonite, due to its perfect cleavage in two directions. Luster, when polished, is vitreous.

In addition to Brazil, sources of cuttable crystals have been found in Australia, Sweden, and the United States. Canada, Mexico, Russia, and South Africa have also yielded rough.

RHODONITE:	Very rare as gem-quality crystal
Major Sources:	South America
Colors Found:	Red, orange-red & pink
Family:	Rhodonite
Hardness:	5.5 to 6.5
Refractive Index:	1.733–1.747
Specific Gravity:	3.50
Crystal System:	Triclinic

Two cabochon rhodonites

Brazilian rhodonite

RUBY

RUBY

The beauty, rarity, and historical mystique of *ruby* is undeniable. It derives its name from the Latin word for red, *rufus*. Ruby is July's birthstone, the gemstone for Capricorns, and the traditional 15th and 40th anniversary gift.

Legends and lore

The historical mystique and beauty of rubies are as colorful as the legends that surround these most precious of gems. The earliest record for the mining of rubies dates to more than 2,500 years ago in Sri Lanka, "the jewel box of the Indian Ocean," where it is called *rathu kata*. Rubies from Sri Lanka first appeared in Western jewelry among the Etruscans (600–275 BC) and were used by the Greeks and Romans from approximately 480 BC onward. For the last thousand years, the most sought-after rubies have come from Burma (known as Myanmar today).

Rubies have been prized throughout history, and many believed that mystical powers lay hidden within these intensely colored red gemstones. The fiery crimson color of rubies caused many civilizations to associate them with passion, love, and romance. Rubies were also thought to bestow wisdom, health, and luck in gambling. According to oriental beliefs, ruby is the "Gem of the Sun." Mentioned in Sanskrit texts, the ancient Hindus were so enchanted by the color of rubies that they called them *ratnaraj*—"the King of Gems." They thought that the colors of rubies were due to an inextinguishable fire that burned inside the gems that would endow their wearers with long life—and would even cause water to boil. As in Sanskrit texts, biblical references to ruby (all red gemstones were also collectively called *carbuncle* at this time) refer to it as a most precious gem. In the King James Version of the Bible, ruby (and its namesake, carbuncle) is mentioned numerous times:

Exodus 28:17
And thou shalt set in it settings of stones, even four rows of stones: the first row shall be a sardius, a topaz, and a carbuncle: this shall be the first row.

Exodus 39:10
And they set in it four rows of stones: the first row was a sardius, a topaz, and a carbuncle: this was the first row.

Ezekiel 28:13
Thou hast been in Eden the garden of God; every precious stone was thy covering, the sardius, topaz, and the diamond, the beryl, the onyx, and the jasper, the sapphire, the emerald, and the carbuncle, and gold: the workmanship of thy tabrets and of thy pipes was prepared in thee in the day that thou wast created.

Isaiah 54:12
And I will make thy windows of agates, and thy gates of carbuncles, and all thy borders of pleasant stones.

Job 28:18
No mention shall be made of coral, or of pearls: for the price of wisdom is above rubies.

Proverbs 3:15
She is more precious than rubies: and all the things thou canst desire are not to be compared unto her.

Proverbs 8:11
For wisdom is better than rubies; and all the things that may be desired are not to be compared to it.

Proverbs 20:15
There is gold, and a multitude of rubies: but the lips of knowledge are a precious jewel.

Lamentations 4:7
Her Nazarites were purer than snow, they were whiter than milk, they were more ruddy in body than rubies, their polishing was of sapphire.

Interestingly, the gems called "rubies" in the Old Testament may have actually been spinel or garnet. Up until the 18th century, when chemical testing was improved, most red gems were called rubies. In fact, many of the famous rubies in the crown jewels of Europe have since been identified as spinel or garnet. For example, the Black Prince's Ruby that rests proudly at the center of the British Imperial State Crown is actually a red spinel.

Ancient Sinhalese (modern-day Sri Lanka) legends relate the story of the destruction of their demonic King Ravana. They believed that after his demise, his blood turned into rubies, resulting in their intense red color.

For over 2,000 years, Sri Lanka has supplied the world with fine star rubies. In fact, Sri Lanka was most probably the original source of this gem. The ancient Sinhalese believed that a star ruby protected the wearer from witchcraft. It was considered so powerful a talisman that even when the original owner passed the gem on to someone else, he continued to receive its protection. In Europe, star rubies were sometimes called *the three swords* and were said to chase away evil, bring good luck, and assist one in finding a fine spouse.

Native Americans believed that offerings of a fine ruby resulted in rebirth as a powerful chief.

Some cultures believed ruby's blood-like color would protect the wearer from injury. In fact, ancient Burmese warriors believed that when a ruby was inserted beneath the skin, it generated a mystical force, making them unconquerable in battle. Rubies were once known by the Burmese as "blood drops from the heart of the mother Earth" and were worn by them as a talisman to protect against illness or misfortune.

Dr. Eduard Gübelin's book, *Burma, Land der Pagoden* (Burma, Land of Pagodas), includes a famous Burmese ruby legend:

One day, the king of the valley, a grand old eagle, was circling over his kingdom and searching for a worthy prey. As he spread his circles ever wider in the shining blue of the heavens, he suddenly spied on the valley floor a piece of fresh meat of the color of purest blood and more enticing than he had ever seen in all his flights throughout the whole world. There is the noble food, for which I have been yearning, said the lord in the air, and plunged down on to his chosen prey. But his claws, whose sharpness and strength had hitherto hooked into the thickest skin, could do nothing against this presumed prey, colored like a living heart. He kept on attacking—he, the lord of the valley, accustomed to victory!—But in vain! He began to fear that age had impaired his strength, so he ascended into the air to think it over. He also sought out other prey in order to test

From left to right: Burmese ruby, Tanzanian ruby, and Madagascan ruby

his strength, but left it lying carelessly as soon as he had convinced himself of his undiminished powers, in order to renew his attack on the coveted piece of booty. Finally, it dawned on him: this was no piece of flesh, but a hallowed stone, fashioned out of fire and the blood of Mother Earth. Reverently, the wise old King of the Birds grasped it and carried it to the highest summit of the highest mountain—unattainable to all living beings on this earth. The valley in which he had found the precious stone was Mogok, and the stone the first ruby in the world.

In the 13th century, renowned explorer Marco Polo wrote that Kublai Khan, the Mongol Emperor of China, once offered an entire city for a ruby the size of a man's finger. And legend had it that a giant ruby once lit an entire chamber in a palace of a Chinese emperor.

In the Middle Ages, rubies were thought to contain prophetic powers. It was believed that a ruby could warn its owner of misfortunes by deepening in color.

Ralph Waldo Emerson, an American essayist, poet, and leader of the transcendentalist movement in the early 19th century, wrote the following poem about rubies:

> They brought me rubies from the mine, and held them to the sun; I said, "They are drops of frozen wine from Eden's vats that run." I look'd again—I thought them hearts of friends, to friends unknown; Tides that should warm each neighboring life are lock'd in sparkling stone. But fire to thaw that ruddy snow, to break enchanted ice, and give love's scarlet tides to flow, when shall that sun arise?

Just the facts

As *allochromatic* (other colored) gems, rubies' colors are due to trace elements. Apart from their color, the gems are identical to sapphires and are comprised of corundum. Corundum is the crystalline form of aluminum oxide. Its name is believed to be derived from three ancient Tamil, Hindi, and Sanskrit words for rubies and sapphires: *kurundam, kurund,* or *kuruvinda,* respectively.

Did you know that rubies are more expensive than diamonds? A 16ct ruby that sold at Sotheby's in New York in October 1988 fetched a staggering US $3,630,000. Rubies are some of the world's most expensive gemstones, but like all gems, quality determines price.

Second only to diamonds in hardness, rubies are some of the toughest gemstones, and with no cleavage, breakage rarely occurs. This, combined with the fact that rubies come in many different shapes and sizes, makes them perfect for all types of jewelry.

Color is the most important factor when evaluating rubies. While cutting and size (fine rubies over two carats are very scarce) are also important, transparency is secondary. Why is this? Colored by chromium, rubies formed millions of years ago deep within the earth. Because very few rubies

Ruby and diamond ring
in yellow gold

Ruby and diamond earrings
in white gold

crystallized undisturbed, a whole host of tiny irregularities (inclusions) is a characteristic of their formation. Far from being flaws, inclusions are a fascinating hallmark of authenticity that record a gem's natural relationship with the earth. In terms of clarity, rubies tend to be less clean than sapphires.

While color preferences are subjective, the best rubies possess an intense, almost electric red effect in daylight due to fluorescence. The ideal ruby displays an intense, rich crimson without being too light or too dark. But as rubies come in many different colors and sizes, ultimately, your personal preference should be your primary concern. Remember, beauty is in the eye of the beholder and will also be tempered by what you can afford.

RUBY:	July's birthstone
Major Sources:	Afghanistan, Burma, Cambodia, India, Kenya, Madagascar, Mozambique, Sri Lanka, Tajikistan, Tanzania, Thailand & Vietnam
Colors Found:	Red
Family:	Corundum: Al_2O_3
Hardness:	9.00
Refractive Index:	1.76–1.78; Uniaxial (–)
Specific Gravity:	3.97–4.05
Crystal System:	Trigonal

Microscopic rutile inclusions, commonly known as *silk*, are a typical characteristic of rubies. When evenly distributed, small quantities of silk enhance a ruby's beauty and value by creating a soft, uniform distribution of sparkling light.

Asterism, or the "star effect," is a reflection effect that appears as two or more intersecting bands of light across the surface of a gem. This rare phenomenon is found in both rubies and sapphires. Asterism in corundum is due to reflections from multitudes of exsolved needle inclusions (silk), which, in most varieties, consist of rutile.

Ruby sources

Burma continues to produce some of the world's finest rubies. While the original locality for rubies was most likely Sri Lanka (Ceylon), the classic source is the Mogok Stone Tract in upper Burma—so much so that one of the recognized titles of the Kings of Burma was "Lord of the Rubies."

While *pigeon's blood* was once used to describe a rare and valuable Burmese ruby color, it has now largely fallen out of use. Burmese rubies come from the Mogok Valley in north-central Burma and Möng Hsu in northeast Burma (pronounced 'mong shu' or 'mine shu').

Möng Hsu is 140 miles southeast of Mogok, between the Nam Pang and Salween rivers. Typical of many areas in Burma's Shan States, the population of the Möng Hsu area consists of Shans

Indian star ruby and diamond bracelet
in 14Kt yellow gold

in the valleys with hill tribes (Palaungs at Möng Hsu) living in the mountains. The Palaungs cultivated tea before the discovery of ruby. While ruby mining in Mogok dates to the 6th century, rubies were not discovered in Möng Hsu until 1991, when a local resident who used to be a ruby miner at Mogok went bathing in the Nam Nga stream and found red gems between his toes and among the pebbles on the river's banks. Thus began Burma's most recent ruby rush as the town's population quadrupled overnight from approximately 8,000 people to over 30,000 at the peak. This tapered off after 1993, but since the advent of high-temperature treatment, Möng Hsu has become an increasingly important source of Burmese ruby. You can learn more about gemstone enhancements in the enhancements section of this guide.

Ruby mining in Burma was initially restricted to alluvial deposits, but now it also involves mining the marble in the surrounding hills. Millions of years of weathering freed the rubies from their host rock, carrying them down from the hills to the valley floors, where they settled in the bottom of the streams and rivers. It is from these ancient alluvial river gravels (known in Burma as *byon*) that the majority of gems have been recovered.

Most Madagascan rubies are mined from a deposit found in 2004. The only way to reach the ruby mines near the mining village of Moramanga is by a grueling long day's trek on a muddy trail through dense rainforest from the Madagascan town of Andilamena. Most of the ruby from this deposit is treated by filling the fissures with a high-refractive index glass.

From left to right: Vietnamese star ruby, Burmese ruby, and Madagascan ruby

An additional deposit of ruby in Madagascar is at Vatomandry. Stones from Vatomandry are often untreated. Apart from Madagascar, rubies are found in India, Kenya, Mozambique, Sri Lanka, Tanzania, Tajikistan, Vietnam, and, of course, Thailand. However, the deposits in Thailand and Cambodia are largely exhausted.

In 2008–09, significant new ruby deposits were discovered in Mozambique, near M'sawize and Namahumbire. Much of this material is treated by glass filling, but some requires no enhancement whatsoever.

With most of the world's ruby production passing though Thailand, our gemstone buyers are among the first to choose the finest examples.

During the 1980s, Australia produced approximately 70% of the world's sapphires, and although production has decreased, international demand for Australian sapphires remains high. Sapphires found in Australia originate from similar geological conditions to those of Thailand, Cambodia, and parts of Madagascar and, thus, possess similar characteristics.

Ceylon sapphire (Sri Lanka)

A renowned source for gemstones, the island of Ceylon (renamed Sri Lanka in 1972) holds the earliest records for the mining of sapphires (known in Sri Lanka as *nilkata*). It has been a classic source of quality sapphires since antiquity and King Solomon reportedly wooed the Queen of Sheba with Sri Lankan sapphires. The gem from Sri Lanka first appeared in Western jewelry among the Etruscans (600–275 BC) and were used by the Greeks and Romans from approximately 480 BC onward.

In Sri Lanka, sapphire mining occurs in the gem-rich alluvial gravels found beneath the tea-covered slopes of Elahera and Ratnapura (which literally means "gem city"). Dating to 2,500 years ago, Ratnapura holds one of the earliest records for the mining of sapphires. Located approximately 62 miles southeast of Sri Lanka's capital city, Colombo, Ratnapura is the main alluvial gem bed found in Sri Lanka. Here, sapphires are found embedded in layers of gravel and sand, in river beds, marshes, and fields or accumulated at the foot of hills. The alluvial deposits are commonly reached by 60- to 100-foot shafts, where the gem-rich gravel layer is laboriously extracted by hand.

Noted for their royal and cornflower blues, *Ceylon sapphires* are synonymous with top quality and are highly coveted. They received a boost in their popularity in 1981, when Prince Charles gave Lady Diana an engagement ring set with a stunning 18ct Ceylon sapphire.

Kanchanaburi sapphire (Thailand)

The province of Kanchanaburi, renowned for the bridge over the River Kwai, rests among the sleepy valleys of western Thailand. Kanchanaburi's Bo Ploi sapphire mines were discovered in 1918 and, today, remain one of world's premier sources of blue sapphires. The sapphires of Bo Ploi are mined from alluvial deposits derived from alkali basalts. The miners there must unearth over 50 tons of alluvial soil to extract just one carat of sapphire crystals. Sapphires have been heavily mined there since the 1980s and are now depleted. This increasing rarity makes these sapphires a must for any jewelry collection.

From left to right: Kanchanaburi sapphire, Madagascan sapphire, and midnight blue sapphire

Madagascan sapphire

Today, Madagascar also provides some of the highest-quality sapphires. The gems were first unearthed on this island in the early 1990s. The Madagascan gem fields now reportedly account for approximately 20% of the world's sapphires. The majority of Madagascar's sapphires come from the prolific gem fields of Ilakaka, as well as Andranondambo, Andrebabe, and Diego Suarez.

Midnight blue sapphire

Midnight blue sapphires combine deep, rich colors and a spellbinding luster all in one gemstone. Deep blues intermingle in midnight blue sapphires as if to reveal the secret of the sky at night. This accentuates their luster and is one reason for their enduring popularity. Mined in a wide variety of countries including Madagascar, Australia, Nigeria, Thailand, Vietnam, and China, midnight blue sapphires possess colors that are beyond vivid. But there is nothing black about midnight blue sapphire. To visualize this, think of the color of a desert sky shortly after the sun has set, with stars rising in the distance. This is the color of midnight blue sapphire, an intense azure hue unmatched in the gem kingdom.

Nigerian sapphire

Nigeria plays a key role in supplying the world with some of the most popular gemstones. Nigerian sapphires are mined at Nisama Jama'a, in Nigeria's Kaduna State.

Pailin sapphire (Cambodia)

The Cambodian city of Pailin (the ancient Khmer word for "blue sapphire") is steeped in local folklore regarding its precious treasures:

> Long ago, people hunting in the forests around Pailin encountered a magical old lady called Yiey Yat (*yiey* means grandmother in Khmer) living as a hermit in the mountains. Fearing for the local wildlife, she told the villagers that if they stopped hunting, the gods would reward them with something of far greater value in the streams and rivers of Mount Yat. The people went there and saw an otter (*pey* in Khmer) playing (*leng* in Khmer) in a stream. Swimming up to them, when the otter opened its mouth, it was full of gems.

As a result, the area and its sapphires are known as *Pey Leng*, which, when translated to Thai, became *Pailin*. Even today, many people visit the shrine of Yiey Yat to ask her for riches.

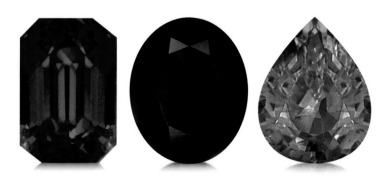

From left to right: Pailin sapphire, Shangdong sapphire, and Umba River sapphire

Star sapphire

With their very bright and lustrous star formations, *star sapphires* have traditionally been the most popular of all star gemstones. Glance at a star sapphire, and you will see six- or even 12-rayed stars silently gliding across the gemstone's surface. This wonderful gem has long been coveted for its beautiful and mysterious optical effect known as *asterism*, or "the star effect." It is caused by sets of parallel needle-like inclusions within the gemstone. While the gem gravels of Sri Lanka and Burma are the world's main sources of star sapphires, black star sapphires are mainly found in Thailand's Chanthaburi province and in Australia.

In many cultures, star sapphires were considered love charms. Helen of Troy was said to have owned a star sapphire and to have owed her conquests to it. In 17th century Germany, star sapphire was the *siegstein*, meaning "victory stone." To others, star sapphire was the "stone of destiny," as its crossing bands of light were believed to represent faith, hope, and destiny. Star sapphires were commonly used as talismans to protect against the evil eye, and the Sinhalese used them to guard against witchcraft. The gems were particularly prized in ancient times as a guiding star for travelers. The famous English traveler Sir Richard Francis Burton possessed a large specimen, which he referred to as his talisman, claiming it brought him good horses and prompt attention wherever he went. In fact, it was only in those places where he received proper attention that he would show it, a favor greatly appreciated because the sight of the gem was believed to bring good luck. One of the most unique of all talismanic gems, star sapphire is said to be so potent that it continues to exercise its good influence over the first wearer even if it has passed into other hands.

Songea sapphire

While they might not have the pinks to be padparadscha, there is nothing about the beauty of Songea sapphires that is lacking. Displaying bright blends of crimson tangerines, reminiscent of an African sunset, *sunset sapphires* (also called *Songea sapphires*) were only discovered in 1992. The world's only sunset sapphire deposit is located 37 miles west of Songea, with the Masuguru district being the main mining area. Discoveries like sunset sapphire have helped Songea become the second most important Tanzanian mining area after Merelani (the home of tanzanite).

From left to right: bottle-green sapphire, lime-green sapphire,
padparadscha sapphire, and hot pink sapphire

White sapphire

The ancient Egyptians associated white sapphire with the all-seeing eye of Horus, while the Greeks linked it to their god Apollo, using it in the prophesying of the oracles at Delphi.

The ancient Greeks unearthed white sapphires from the island of Naxos in the Aegean Sea.

With none of the iron, chromium, titanium, and other trace elements that give sapphires their unique colors, white sapphire is arguably sapphire in its purest form. Displaying an exceptional luster and brilliance, it has become a popular alternative to diamond.

From left to right: purple sapphire, yellow sapphire, orange sapphire, and white sapphire

Yellow sapphire and channel-set diamond ring in white gold

Orange sapphire and diamond pendant in yellow gold

SILLIMANITE

Beautiful and rare, *sillimanite* is named for the famous American geologist Benjamin Silliman (1779–1864). The gem is sometimes referred to as *fibrolite*. Sillimanite is not only scarce, but also difficult for miners to identify and problematic for cutters. These three attributes combine to ensure that sillimanite remains a true exotic gemstone.

Just the facts

Sillimanite is formed from aluminum silicate and is usually found as silky, fibrous crystals suitable for cabochons. Transparent crystals suitable for faceting display a glassy luster and are exceedingly scarce. Sillimanite is colorless, white, brown, yellow, blue, and green in color.

Sillimanite is typically found scattered within layers of metamorphic rocks that have been put under great pressure and high temperature. This is why it is commonly found in volcanic or hot spring areas. Because of the way it is scattered within the host rocks, miners often have difficulty in detecting it.

SILLIMANITE:	Has the same chemical make up as kyanite and andalusite
Major Sources:	Worldwide; gem quality: Burma, India & Sri Lanka
Colors Found:	Green, blue-green, blue, yellow, yellow-green, gray, brown & colorless
Family:	Sillimanite
Hardness:	6.5 to 7.5
Refractive Index:	1.655–1.684
Specific Gravity:	3.23–3.27
Crystal System:	Orthorhombic

Sillimanite is a polymorph with two other minerals, *kyanite* and *andalusite*. (A polymorph is a mineral that shares the same chemistry but a different crystal structure with another mineral.) Due to its brittleness, sillimanite is very difficult to facet. Some 50% of gem-quality crystals can be damaged during the faceting and fashioning process alone.

Some sillimanite crystals demonstrate *chatoyancy*, or the "cat's-eye effect" (caused by parallel inclusions reflecting a single band of light back to the eye), and *asterism* ("the star effect" (caused by intersecting inclusions reflecting a star of light back to the eye). These optical effects are highly coveted and well suited for cabochon rings and earrings.

Sillimanite

Greenish yellow Sri Lankan sillimanite

SPHALERITE

A rare treasure for gemstone collectors, *sphalerite* is not well suited for jewelry due to issues of durability. It is soft and has perfect cleavage in multiple directions. It is a difficult gem to cut and polish. The most spectacular property of this mineral is its dispersion, which far exceeds that of diamond and has few peers in the realm of gemstones. Lighter stones demonstrate exceptional fire. In addition to its high dispersion, sphalerite exhibits adamantine luster when properly polished.

Just the facts

Sphalerite is a zinc sulfide that contains varying percentages of iron. While many localities worldwide produce excellent mineral specimens, availability of gem-quality rough for cutting is quite scarce, making gemstones highly sought after by collectors.

Luster varies considerably by habit and chemistry and can range from dull to resinous on fine-grained aggregates or vitreous to resinous on specimens with crystal faces. Sphalerite's incredibly high refractive index (approx. 2.370) is responsible for its adamantine luster when well polished.

Color for sphalerite includes the full spectrum from yellow to red, and it is commonly seen in various shades from yellow to green. As iron content increases, the stone becomes darker, appearing brown to black and exhibiting a metallic luster.

Sphalerite is an important source of zinc ore. Many sources can be found worldwide, but only a small number provide material of gem quality. Spain and Mexico are the two most notable sources of fine-quality rough; however, cuttable material can also be found in Canada, Germany, and the United States.

SPHALERITE:	Has dispersion three times higher than diamond
Major Sources:	Spain, USA, Germany, Mexico, Switzerland & Peru
Colors Found:	Yellow, orange, green, red, brown & black; can be zoned
Family:	Sphalerite
Hardness:	3.5 to 4.0
Refractive Index:	2.37–2.43
Specific Gravity:	3.90–4.10
Crystal System:	Cubic

Yellow, orange, and red sphalerite

SPHENE

Sphene **is named after the Greek word for "wedge" because its crystals are typically wedge shaped. As it contains titanium, sphene is also sometimes referred to by its mineral name,** *titanite.*

One of the world's newest and rarest gems, sphene possesses the rather unusual ability to take a beam of light and break it into all of the spectral colors, a feature gemologically referred to as *fire* or *dispersion*. In this regard, sphene is superior to diamond. This, combined with its strong pleochroism (different colors are displayed when the gemstone is viewed from different angles), has the effect of making the gem appear to change color. Occasionally pink, black, or chocolate, most sphene is predominantly green or yellowish green, with just about every other color of the rainbow displayed by its intense, fiery brilliance.

Just the facts

These are gorgeously brilliant, fiery gems that have a higher dispersion (fire) than diamonds.

Sphene's magnificent fire, unique color shades, strong pleochroism, adamantine (diamond-like) luster, and double refraction (birefringence) make it ideal for earrings and pendants that catch the light, displaying its sparkling qualities to full effect. A unique characteristic of sphene is birefringence (doubly refraction), meaning that light splits into two rays as it passes through the gem. As a result, the back facets appear as double images, giving it a beautiful, soft, hazy appearance—similar to the doubling seen in zircon.

SPHENE:	Fire greater than diamond
Major Sources:	Brazil, Madagascar, Mexico, Pakistan & Sri Lanka
Colors Found:	Yellowish green, orange
Family:	Sphene: $CaTiSiO_5$
Hardness:	5 to 5.5
Refractive Index:	1.84–2.11; Biaxial (+)
Specific Gravity:	3.52–3.54
Crystal System:	Monoclinic

If well polished, the luster can approach or equal that of diamond; however, sphene is notoriously difficult to polish well. A well-polished sphene is testament to an experienced jeweler. At JTV, we always take great care to ensure that our sphene is finished in a manner that maximizes its intense, natural beauty. Sphene that is larger than a few carats and without inclusions is extremely scarce.

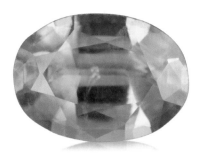

Brazilian sphene

Madagascan sphene

SPINEL

SPINEL

Spinel **was once mistaken for ruby and sapphire, but it's no impostor; instead, it is a "master of disguise." One of the gem kingdom's best-kept secrets, it is treasured for its eternal brilliance and spectacular colors. Whether your fascination with gems is for their beauty, rarity, or history, spinel is a superb addition to your jewelry collection.**

Spinel's name is derived either from the Latin word for "thorn," *spina*, as a result of its characteristic octahedral crystals having pointed ends, or from the Greek word for "spark," *spintharis*, in reference to the gem's bright red hues.

Legends and lore

Due to their mistaken identity, spinels have few historical references. However, they have a bizarre association with sorcerers and alchemists. Spinels were used by practitioners of the "dark arts" to summon demons and were also used as amulets to protect them from fire. One tale describes how spinels could be used to work against their masters. Those who were thought to possess supernatural powers were found guilty if they began to shake when approached with a spinel wrapped in paper.

Spinels occupy a unique place in gemstone history. Despite being recognized as a separate gem species in 1587, up until the 19th century, the intense coloration displayed by red spinel led some to mistakenly identify it as ruby. The source of confusion stemmed not only from color similarities, but also the close proximity of their deposits. It was not until 1783 that Rome de L'Isle became the first scientist to clearly distinguish differences between ruby and red spinel.

SPINEL:	Once confused with ruby and sapphire
Major Sources:	Burma, Madagascar, Sri Lanka, Tajikistan, Tanzania & Vietnam
Colors Found:	Various
Family:	Spinel: $MgAl_2O_4$
Hardness:	8
Refractive Index:	1.71–1.72; SR
Specific Gravity:	3.54–3.63
Crystal System:	Cubic

Red spinel's near-identical resemblance to ruby results in it being a prodigious, albeit accidental, feature in many of the world's most famous gem collections, including the Vatican's and the Crown Jewels of Russia, Iran, and England. Interestingly, both the legendary 352ct Timur Ruby and the 170ct Black Prince's Ruby, which are featured in the British Imperial State Crown, proved to be red spinel.

In 1415 at the Battle of Agincourt, English King Henry V wore a helmet garnished with jewels, including the Black Prince's Ruby. During the battle, the French commander, the Duke of Alencon, struck Henry's head a mighty blow with his battle-ax, nearly killing the King. Surprisingly, the force of the blow glanced off the spinel, saving his life and allowing Henry to lead his troops to what many thought would be an impossible victory.

Just the facts

The reality behind red spinel's ruby-like appearance is its proximity to corundum deposits (the base mineral of rubies and sapphires) and chromium (the Midas element responsible for giving both red spinels and rubies their deep red colors).

Today, spinels can be easily identified by their refractivity. Since red spinels are singly refractive and rubies are doubly refractive, the primary color in red spinels appears purer and more intense than the red seen in many rubies.

Spinel occurs in many colors, including red, blue, pink, orange, and a plethora of other fancy hues.

Similar to rubies, spinels are mined from alluvial deposits generally derived from weathered marbles. They come from a handful of sources, including Tajikistan, Sri Lanka, Madagascar, Tunduru in Tanzania's remote southeast, and central Vietnam's Luc Yen region. While most gemstone aficionados know Burma to be the classic and most familiar source for fine red spinels,

Ayanna Spinel	Red to pink spinel from Mahenge, Tanzania
Balas Ruby	A historical name for spinel, which referred to gems from the Kuh-i-Lal mine in Badakhshan in present-day Tajikistan
Cobalt Blue Spinel	Resembling fine sapphire, this exceptional blue spinel from Sri Lanka, Tanzania, and Vietnam is sometimes colored by cobalt. Regular blue spinel also hails from Tanzania and displays visual similarities to sapphire, particularly those from Montana, USA
Flame Spinel	The orange-red variety of spinel
Gahnite or Gahnospinel	Named after Swedish chemist L.G. Gahn; the rare greenish or bluish, zinc-rich variety of spinel
Red Spinel	The red variety of spinel that was historically mistaken for ruby

new discoveries in Tanzania's Mahenge region are shifting paradigms. Tanzanian red spinel is increasingly acclaimed for its bright red hues and a brilliance and luster that defy verbal description.

Perfect octahedral crystals are sometimes set into jewelry in their original, uncut octahedral shapes. The Burmese refer to these gems as *nat thwe*, meaning "spirit polished." Sometimes *nat thwe* spinels will receive a very light polishing.

Pure spinel is white, but impurities give it a wide range of colors. Almost all of them are used in jewelry. The most valuable and popular color, though, is red. Occasionally, color-change varieties are found, turning from a light gray-blue in daylight to a light purple under candlelight. Star spinels are also known, particularly from Sri Lanka. They may show both four- and six-rayed stars, even on the same stone. Cat's-eye spinels are extremely rare, with only a handful of specimens known.

Did you know that even though they are more affordable, spinels are rarer than rubies? In the gem kingdom, "rare" can be both a blessing and a curse because it affects market prices and availability. This is unfortunate for the spinel miner, but great news for everyone else since the gems are some of nature's most beautiful treasures.

Ayanna red spinel crystal from Tanzania

Custom-cut Sri Lankan purple spinel

of Merelani that rise from the hot plains at the foot of Mount Kilimanjaro. Running at an angle of 41 degrees to the surface, the deposit line or horizon periodically folds over itself, creating pockets of tanzanite.

Barely covering eight square miles, the tanzanite deposit has been divided into four blocks by the Tanzanian government—Blocks A through D. Block D simply refers to the area from which material is mined. Traditionally, larger quantities of the best material were found in Block D, so the term became synonymous with the top grade. However, fine tanzanite comes from all blocks.

Even at the largest and most sophisticated mine in operation in Block C, the yield for raw tanzanite crystals averages only 22 carats (4.4 grams) per processed ton. Tanzanite production is slowly but surely decreasing, and many experts believe the gemstone will disappear in years to come. Understandably, this has led to tanzanite gaining considerable notoriety. After all, the desire to own something beautiful and rare is irresistible.

Although there are several tanzanite grading systems available, they are all primarily concerned with judging color quality. Traditionally, miners described the finest, most richly colored stones as AAA.

Round tanzanite

Compared to ruby, sapphire, and emerald, tanzanite is typically free from inclusions, making color the single most important evaluation factor. Representing less than one percent of all tanzanite mined, top-shelf tanzanite is characterized by intensely deep indigo blues that most sapphires only dream of.

As the gems typically start their lives as bluish burgundy crystals, virtually all tanzanites have been heated to enhance their color. This is an accepted and permanent treatment that actually makes tanzanite's color-causing element, vanadium, more stable. Occasionally, this process produces highly coveted and extremely rare fancy colors (pink tanzanite, green tanzanite, bi-color tanzanite, etc.). Possessing all the qualities of regular tanzanites, these colored varieties are far less common and are highly coveted by collectors.

Tanzanite exudes sophistication, individuality, and self-confidence. Tanzanite jewelry is suited to all ages, emphasizing the nonconformity of the young and the sophistication of the mature. However, tanzanite is rare and growing rarer by the moment.

18Kt white gold tanzanite & diamond ring

Apart from the sheer pleasure of owning one of the 20th century's most spectacular gemstones, those fortunate to already own it (or to purchase one before the only known deposit is depleted) truly are custodians of a gem whose legacy will be to pass it on as an heirloom to future generations.

Tanzanite specimen

TEKTITE & MOLDAVITE

We are not alone. Since the beginning of time, the curiosity of human-kind has been aroused by the descent of "shooting stars" or meteorites into our world. So catch a falling star as we discover the mystery behind this extraterrestrial gemstone...

Tektite comes from the Greek word *tektos*, meaning "molten," and was the name given by Edward Suess, a professor at the University of Vienna.

A *meteor* is a small particle from space that appears as a bright light that completely burns up before it hits the ground. However, a *meteorite* is a meteor that is large enough to reach the ground without burning up completely. Frequently exploding on impact and throwing pieces of rare, highly sought-after meteorite debris over a large area, these incredibly scarce and collectible gems are perfect for anyone fascinated by outer space.

Just the facts

Collectively known as *tektites*, they are assigned names based on their location. Thus, *moldavites*, named after the Moldu river in the Czech Republic, are found in that country (as well as Austria and Germany), *australites* are from Australia, *philippinites* are from the Philippines and southern China, *malaysianites* are from Malaysia, and *indochinites* are from Thailand, Burma, China, Laos, and Vietnam.

Considered to be gemstones from space, tektites are fragments of natural glass that are formed from meteorite impacts with our planet. Tektites come in two forms. The more typical

TEKTITE:	Extraterrestrial gem
Major Sources:	Australia, Austria, China, Czech Republic, Germany, Laos, Malaysia, Philippines, Thailand & Vietnam
Colors Found:	Black, brown & green
Family:	Tektite
Hardness:	5.5
Refractive Index:	1.48–1.54; SR
Specific Gravity:	2.32–2.38
Crystal System:	Amorphous

"splash form" tektites have rounded, aerodynamic shapes like spheres, teardrops, dumbbells, and disks, while "layered" tektites are usually only found in Southeast Asia and have blocky, fragmental shapes, often displaying compositional layering.

Tektite from Indonesia

Some tektites are smooth, but others have rough, strongly eroded surfaces. Most are jet black; moldavites, however, are dark to bottle green and are usually the most suitable for faceting. Tektites look similar to obsidian, which is a result of volcanic lava coming into contact with water, but they are differentiated by their color and chemical composition.

Tektites are only found in a few regions on earth (called "tektite-strewn fields") and are, in most cases, associated with young impact craters on or near land.

Moldavite

Considered a blend of heaven and earth, this silica-rich tektite is still one of the mysteries of the universe. It was discovered in the late 1700s in western Moravia (now Czech Republic), near the Moldau River. The locality lends its name to this amazing gemstone.

Just the facts

Moldavite is a natural glass, but unlike obsidian, it is not formed by volcanic activity. There is still speculation as to how it formed, but many scientists now believe that it is the result of a meteorite impact with Earth. Thus, moldavite can be considered both terrestrial and extraterrestrial in origin.

Chemically, moldavite is silica containing oxides of iron and aluminum. Color can range from green to olive green or green-brown. The brownish component is due to the presence of iron oxide. Although relatively unknown to the consumer, moldavite has gained considerable popularity in recent years. Unfortunately, demand has put increased pressure on what is considered a very limited supply of this exotic gem.

MOLDAVITE:	Beautiful green tektite from Czech Republic
Major Sources:	Czech Republic
Colors Found:	Green, yellowish green
Family:	Moldavite
Hardness:	5.5–6.5
Refractive Index:	1.490
Specific Gravity:	2.36
Crystal System:	Amorphous

Moldavite

Moldavite specimen

TIGER'S EYE

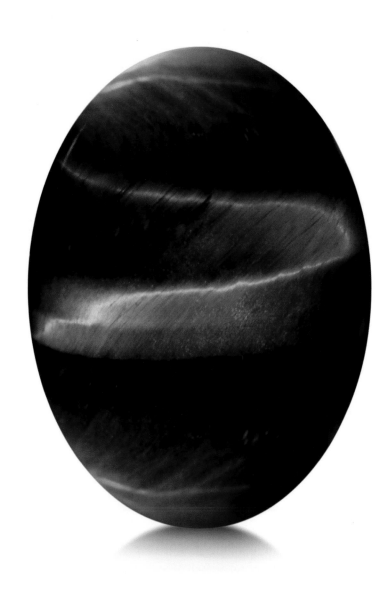

TIGER'S EYE

The best-known variety of chatoyant quartz (or cat's-eye quartz), *cat's eye* is appropriately named. Also called *crocidolite cat's eye* or *African cat's eye*, cat's eye has rich yellow and golden brown stripes, with a fine golden luster when polished.

Legends and lore

Coveted since antiquity, Roman soldiers wore cat's eye for protection in battle. Due to its appearance, in the ancient world, cat's eye was thought to be all-seeing, offering protection during travel and strengthening convictions and confidence.

Many legends say that wearing cat's eye is beneficial for health and spiritual well-being. Legend also says it is a psychic protector, it is great for business, and it aids in achieving clarity of mind.

Today, crystal healers use cat's eye for focusing the mind.

Just the facts

Quartz gemstones are commonly separated into two groups based on the size of their individual crystals. The macrocrystalline quartz (large crystal) group includes many popular

TIGER'S EYE:	Chatoyancy
Major Sources:	Australia, Brazil, India, Namibia & South Africa
Colors Found:	Blue-green, golden brown, green-gray & reddish brown
Family:	Quartz: SiO_2
Hardness:	6.5 to 7
Refractive Index:	1.53–1.54
Specific Gravity:	2.58–2.64
Crystal System:	Trigonal (aggregate)

gemstones such as cat's eye, amethyst, ametrine, and citrine. Cryptocrystalline quartz includes species whose individual crystals are too small to be easily distinguished. Apart from being a variety within the group, *chalcedony* is also a catchall term to describe cryptocrystalline quartz and includes many gems that have been coveted since antiquity.

Cat's eye is a pseudomorph (the result of one mineral replacing another) that contains oriented fibers of crocidolite that have been replaced by silica.

Cat's eye displays chatoyancy (a vertical, luminescent band like that of a cat's eye). While cat's eye typically has lustrous, alternating yellow or brown bands, varieties of chatoyant quartz include a blue-green variety called *hawk's eye quartz*, a greenish gray variety called *cat's-eye quartz*, and a reddish brown variety called *bull's-eye quartz* or *ox eye quartz*. Cutting is crucial with cat's eye because the rough crystals reveal little or nothing of the chatoyancy of the finished gem.

Tiger's eye

Hawk's eye

TOPAZ

TOPAZ

The origin of the name *topaz* generates confusion because some references point to the Sanskrit word *tapaz*, meaning "fire," while others believe it is named after Zeberget, an island in the Red Sea that the Greeks called *Topazius*, the ancient source of peridot.

While some sources think this was due to ancient confusion between topaz and peridot, it now appears more likely that this name might have come from confusion with the Greek word *topasin*, which means "to guess" or "conjecture," possibly in reference to the way fishermen sometimes lost the island in fog. Regardless, in history, the name was not consistently or specifically applied (it was once used to describe most yellow gems), and sometimes topaz and peridot are mentioned as being the same and sometimes different. Interestingly, in the famous book *The Curious Lore of Precious Stones*, the esteemed gemologist George Frederick Kunz (1856–1932) states that these two gems are the same species.

Topaz is an inherently romantic gem and features regularly in the titles of romance novels and honeymoon destinations. Its name indicates beauty, rarity, and wealth, and it imparts a sense of timelessness.

While the golden yellow and blues of topaz are the most widely known, it actually comes in a diverse array of striking colors. This, combined with its beauty and durability, makes topaz jewelry ideal for all occasions.

Legends and lore

Many ancient traditions and beliefs have created a brilliant history for topaz. Like peridot, the Egyptians called topaz the "Gem of the Sun," believing it was colored by the golden glow of their sun god, Ra, and, thus, a powerful protector from harm.

Greeks and Romans also associated the golden crystals with their sun god, Jupiter. They believed the gem increased their strength and could neutralize enchantments.

Topaz is mentioned in the Bible as being one of the "stones of fire" (Ezekiel 28:13–16) that

TOPAZ:	November's birthstone
Major Sources:	Brazil, Burma, Mexico, Mozambique, Nigeria, Russia & Sri Lanka
Colors Found:	Various
Family:	Topaz: $Al_2SiO_4(F,OH)_2$
Hardness:	8
Refractive Index:	1.60–1.64; Biaxial (+)
Specific Gravity:	3.49–3.57
Crystal System:	Orthorhombic

were given to Moses and set in the breastplate of Aaron (Exodus 28:15–30). Topaz is also one of the 12 gemstones set in the foundations of the city walls of Jerusalem (Revelations 21:19) and associated with the Apostle Matthew.

Bushmen in Africa used topaz in healing ceremonies and rituals to connect with ancestral spirits.

In medieval courts, kings, judges, and other noble persons were often presented with an engraved topaz to win favor and cultivate positive relationships.

If you are on a journey of spiritual change, topaz is believed by crystal healers to make an excellent companion. It apparently teaches you to trust in the universe, aiding you to fully recognize the magical laws of attraction, increasing your ability to manipulate them.

Once believed to make you invincible during danger, topaz is also believed by some crystal healers to strengthen confidence and to help you make correct decisions by giving you the courage to follow through on choices, thereby changing dreams into reality.

Meditations with topaz are believed by some to help awaken sleeping talents and illuminate co-creative energies.

Just the facts

Mined from both host rock and alluvial deposits, its unique crystal structure makes topaz a hard and dense gemstone. Because of this, pure colorless topaz has often been mistaken for diamond. Weighing 1,680 carats, the huge Braganza gemstone, mounted into the Portuguese crown jewels, was originally thought to be a diamond—in fact, it is a beautiful clear topaz.

A hydrous aluminum fluorosilicate, topaz is usually formed in granitic pegmatites and in quartz veins.

From left to right: sky blue topaz, Swiss blue topaz, and London blue topaz

Blue topaz

Blue topaz exists in a wide range of shades. The lightest color is known as *sky blue* and is often described as subtle, soft, or pastel. In appearance, it is similar to the color of aquamarine (a precious variety of beryl), and for that reason, it is often used as an affordable alternative to the latter.

As color intensifies, another designation comes into play—*Swiss blue*. It is a deeper, richer shade that offers another alternative for gem lovers. Some of the finest Swiss blue is often described as *neon* or *electric* and is given the special name *super blue* to describe its exceptional color.

The final designation, *London blue*, refers to the deepest, richest shade in the blue topaz series. Jewelry Television's *Barehipani topaz* embodies the finest quality of this highly popular member of the topaz family.

Glacier Topaz™

A unification of fire and ice, *Glacier Topaz*™ mixes the pure clear whites of glacier ice with a fiery brilliance and luster reminiscent of diamonds. Sourced from Russia's frozen wildness, Glacier Topaz™ is a stunning new gemstone exclusive to JTV.

Mined from the same region as Russian alexandrite and Siberian emerald, Glacier Topaz™ is yet another testament to the quality of Russian gemstones. Glacier Topaz™, arguably topaz at its most pure, requires only cutting and faceting to reveal its hidden beauty.

Glacier Topaz™ is mined at one location on the planet—the famous Murzinka mines (named after the Ostyak's Prince Murzin) in the Ural Mountains, Russia. Active for well over a century, the Murzinka mines produce some of the world's finest topaz, a gemstone for which Russia was once famous.

Bi-color tourmaline should not be confused with *watermelon tourmaline*. Watermelon tourmaline is a crystal with the inner part showing pink surrounded by green. It is typically thinly sliced in sections, like a loaf of bread, and polished to show the "watermelon" effect.

Paraíba tourmaline

The world was introduced to *paraíba tourmaline* by Brazilian miner Heitor Dimas Barbosa in 1989. Convinced there were fine stones in the hills of the Brazilian state of Paraíba, he took five years before unearthing his first paraíba tourmaline crystal.

While paraíba tourmalines were first found in Brazil's Paraíba State, stones of similar color and composition have now been found in the neighboring Rio Grande do Norte State (Brazil). The first African find was discovered in 2001 at the Edoukou mine in Oyo (Nigeria), close to the border of Benin. Also in 2001, yucca root farmers in Mozambique's Nampula Province discovered paraíba tourmalines. This material did not hit the market in a big way until 2006.

When paraíba tourmaline was first discovered in Brazil, the unusually intense "neon" or "electric" colors set it apart from any other tourmaline previously known. The color of this gem ranges from intense emerald green to Windex blue to a rich sapphire blue, and continuing along the spectrum to indigo, intense violet (similar to fine amethyst), purple, and even red. Apart from the intense colors, a key feature of these gems is their relative lack of extinction.

Paraíba tourmaline is extremely brilliant, glowing even in low light. It displays electric Windex blues, neon peacocks, sizzling turquoises, or dazzling twilight blues. While personal preferences play a part, traditionally, the Windex blues are the most coveted. Top Brazilian paraíbas can fetch as much as $20,000/ct or more in the wholesale gem market. Fine African gems can also be worth thousands of dollars per carat, making the African stone a tremendous value.

Paraíba tourmaline owes its spectacular colors to small amounts of copper, with manganese and iron. Higher quantities of copper produce more blue and turquoise colors, while elevated manganese gives more violet and red hues. Iron is thought to be a factor coloring the greens.

Does every tourmaline that contains a certain amount of copper/manganese/iron qualify as a paraíba? In a word, no. The most important feature of a paraíba tourmaline is exactly that which made the gem famous in the first place—intensity of color. Gems that lack the requisite color intensity or those with too much extinction should not be sold as *paraíba*. JTV markets those lighter colors under the name *Mozambique* tourmaline.

From left to right: two colors of paraíba tourmaline and rubellite tourmaline

Paraíba tourmaline is typically a richly colored gem that displays electric Windex blues, neon peacocks, and sizzling turquoises. Initially discovered at Mina da Bathalha, Paraíba, Brazil, it possesses an intense color that allows the gem to glow and shine even when there is little light.

While most paraíba tourmaline is under one carat, gems from Mozambique come in sizes of up to 40 carats or more. Like emeralds, inclusions are common in paraíba tourmaline, making its color the main beauty determinant. However, when paraíba tourmaline is clean, its rarity and value increase exceptionally. Its beautiful vivid colors have made paraíba tourmaline hugely popular within a short time. One of the world's most desired gemstones, paraíba tourmaline is a gem whose impossible rarity is only surpassed by its unrivaled beauty.

Rubellite tourmaline

Rubellite's sensuous mélange is the personification of seduction; no other colors display its comparable flair. Whispering in passionate pinks and suggestive purples, rubellite affords the perfect romance in an opulence of red. The gem, deriving its name from the Latin word *rubellus*, meaning "coming from red," is a lustrous, reddish pink and purple-toned variety of tourmaline. In the 17th century, the Tsar of Russia commissioned many items of gemstone jewelry to be made for the Imperial Crown Court. However, gems that were originally thought to be rubies have later been discovered to be rubellite.

Extremely rare, rubellite has taken the jewelry world by storm in recent years, following the discovery of new deposits. Madagascan rubellite heralds from mines located 26 miles from the town of Betafo, in the Antananarivo province in Madagascar's central highlands. Interestingly, this deposit produces some truly unique rubellites, whose color is close to that of famous rubies.

Major rubellite finds date from the 19th century, when they were discovered in Brazil. This country continues to be a major supplier, particularly in Minas Gerais state. Some of the finest stones came from Ouro Fino, in Coronel, Murta (Minas Gerais). Discovered about 1983, by 1985, the deposit was already exhausted. Ouro Fino rubellite acquired legendary status in the gem world.

Surprisingly enough, Southern California's Pala District was also once an important source, particularly in the late 19th and early 20th centuries. The blue-capped rubellite crystals from the Tourmaline Queen mine are world famous among mineral collectors.

In the summer of 1998, a new tourmaline deposit was discovered in a farming area 25 miles from the ancient city of Ibadan, in Nigeria, West Africa. This material was exceptionally clean and well saturated. Within just a few short years, over 1000 kg of rough was taken out of the ground, and just as quickly as it appeared, it was gone.

In 2007, another major find was made, this time near Chimoio, Mozambique (near the border with Zimbabwe), with colors similar to Nigeria.

With the exception of ruby and red spinel, rubellite is the only other gemstone that occurs in such a rich, dark red color. Similar to emerald, inclusions in rubellite are common. The chemical element that colors rubellite (manganese) actually causes a growing crystal to become internally flawed (i.e., the more manganese present, the darker the red color and the more imperfect the final crystal). It is, therefore, extremely rare to find a richly colored rubellite that is internally clean. Rubellites also tend to have more natural inclusions because they are formed near the center of the crystal pocket and, thus, receive more stress and pressure during their formation. Regardless, rubellite is a durable gemstone well suited to everyday jewelry.

TREMOLITE

The rare mineral *tremolite* derives its name from a locality in the Swiss Alps. Its discovery was attributed to a find in the Val Tremola, an area known to travellers as the "Valley of Trembling," due to the precarious roadway that descends its steep slopes. It was later determined that the original material did not originate in the Val Tremola, but another area not too far removed.

Legends and lore

The tremolite offered by JTV was an opportunity find after our buyers became trapped in East Africa during the Icelandic volcanic eruption of 2010. When visiting with dealers in the Arusha buying district, one of the vendors had a small bag of green rough in the back of his vault. He had purchased the rough believing it to be tsavorite, but once tested, discovered it was another mineral—tremolite. This rough was a rare find from the tanzanite mining fields.

Just the facts

The mineral tremolite is a member of the amphibole group and forms a series to ferroactinolite, an iron-rich end member. Chemically, it is a calcium magnesium silicate, but it is rarely pure in nature. Most tremolite contains a small percentage of iron, which is responsible for its greenish color. A beautiful, manganese-rich variety of tremolite, known as *hexagonite*, ranges from pink to purple. Other colors include white to black (opaque material), light yellow, brown, and colorless.

Tremolite forms through low-grade metamorphic processes, which is usually an indicator that high temperature did not exist. Rich green, transparent crystals are rare and, when available, rarely produce gemstones in excess of one carat. Polish luster on transparent gems is vitreous, but it is silky to pearly on fibrous varieties. Fibrous varieties include nephrite and byssolite, the latter being responsible for horsetail inclusions, which are highly prized in Russian demantoid garnets.

Sources of tremolite include Australia, Canada, China, France, Germany, Italy, Norway, Switzerland, and the United States. However, transparent green and reddish material is extremely rare and only available sporadically in the gem trade.

Tremolite

TREMOLITE:	Named for the Tremola Valley, Switzerland
Major Sources:	Canada, Finland, Kenya, Pakistan & USA
Colors Found:	Green, gray, brown, pink, white & colorless
Family:	Tremolite
Hardness:	5.0 to 6.0
Refractive Index:	1.599–1.637
Specific Gravity:	2.95–3.07
Crystal System:	Monoclinic

TURQUOISE

TURQUOISE

The name *turquoise* is derived from the French *pierre turquois,* meaning "Turkish stone." This is because western Europeans mistakenly thought the gem came from Turkey.

In fact, it came from the Sinai Peninsula or the Alimersai Mountain in Persia (now Iran), which has been mining turquoise since 5000 BC. In Persian, turquoise is known as *ferozah*, meaning "victorious," and it is the national gemstone of Iran to this day.

Legends and lore

Turquoise was one of the first gemstones ever mined, dating back to 6000 BC in Egypt's Sinai Peninsula.

In ancient times, the Egyptians, Persians, Mongols, and Tibetans all valued turquoise highly. The first millennium AD saw a big increase in the popularity of turquoise, with both the Chinese and Native Americans becoming captivated by this blue gem.

Turquoise has been used for thousands of years as jewelry by the ancient Egyptians, who buried fine pieces with mummies. When the tomb of Queen Zer was unearthed in 1900, a turquoise and gold bracelet was found on her wrist, making this one of the oldest pieces of jewelry on earth.

The Persians preferred sky blue turquoise, and, as a result, the term "Persian turquoise" is sometimes incorrectly used as a color grade, not as a geographical indicator.

In Mexico, the Aztecs began mining turquoise between 900–1000 AD, often fashioning it into elaborate masks.

The Anasazi people of America mined turquoise in what are now Arizona, New Mexico, and Colorado. The city of Chaco Canyon became very wealthy based on the turquoise trade, which was often exchanged for the feathers of tropical birds. Turquoise from this area found its way around the trade routes of the American continent and has been unearthed as far away as the great Mayan city of Chichén Itzá in the Yucatán. By the 16th century, the cultures of the American southwest were using turquoise as currency.

In North America, the Zuni people of New Mexico have created striking turquoise jewelry set in silver, once believing these protected them from demons. The Navajo believed that turquoise had fallen from the sky and, thus, also protected them from demons, while Apache warriors believed that wearing turquoise improved their hunting prowess. Apache legend has it that if turquoise was affixed to a bow, the arrows shot from it would always hit their mark. All these tribes believed that turquoise brought good fortune and happiness.

European interest in turquoise can be dated to around 500 BC, when the people of Siberia began using the gem; It did not make an impact on western European fashion, though, until the late Middle Ages, when trading with the Near and Middle East increased.

While the Chinese had some mines in their empire, they imported most of their turquoise from Persians, Turks, Tibetans, and Mongols. In Asia, it was considered protection against the evil eye. Tibetans carved turquoise into ritual objects, as well as wearing it in traditional jewelry. Ancient manuscripts from Persia, India, Afghanistan, and Arabia reported that the health of a person wearing turquoise could be assessed by variations in the color of the gem. Turquoise was also thought to promote prosperity.

It is also believed that turquoise helps one to start new projects and protects the wearer from falling, especially from horses. In Europe, even today, turquoise rings are still given as forget-me-not gifts.

Moctezuma's treasure, now displayed in the British Museum, includes a fantastic carved serpent covered by a mosaic of turquoise. In ancient Mexico, turquoise was reserved for the gods; it could not be worn by mere mortals.

Just the facts

Turquoise, a hydrated phosphate of copper and aluminum, is prized as a gemstone whose intense blue color is often mottled with veins of brown limonite or black manganese oxide (commonly known as *spider's web turquoise*). It is almost always opaque and polished as cabochons, but rare, translucent gems also exist.

TURQUOISE:	December's birthstone
Major Sources:	China, India, Iran, Mexico, Tibet & USA
Colors Found:	Bluish green & sky blue
Family:	Turquoise: $CuAl_6(PO_4)_4(OH)_8$
Hardness:	5 to 6
Refractive Index:	1.61–1.65
Specific Gravity:	2.31–2.84
Crystal System:	Triclinic (aggregate)

Turquoise jewelry in the USA has long been produced by Native Americans (Zuni and Navajo peoples). Today, turquoise is prominently associated with Native American culture, particularly Zuni bracelets, Navajo concha belts, squash blossom necklaces, and thunderbird motifs. Native American jewelry with turquoise mounted in or with silver is actually relatively new. Some believe this style of jewelry was unknown prior to about 1880, when a white trader persuaded a Navajo craftsman to make turquoise and silver jewelry using coin silver.

Spider web turquoise

Four flavors of turquoise

VESUVIANITE

Also known by the name *idocrase*, *vesuvianite* was discovered on the slopes of Mt. Vesuvius, Italy. Its name is an allusion to the locality. Highly prized by collectors, this greenish mineral is infrequently seen in the form of gemstones since fine-quality specimens are rarely sacrificed to the lapidary's wheel.

Just the facts

Vesuvianite is a complex mineral (calcium magnesium iron aluminum silicate hydroxide) with a variable chemical formula. Many elemental replacements are possible, the most common being ferrous and ferric iron. Other possibilities include boron, beryllium, sodium, fluorine, and manganese. This variability in chemistry gives rise to a wider-than-normal array of values for various properties.

Vesuvianite is moderately hard but slightly brittle, requiring care when setting in jewelry. Gems, when properly cut, exhibit good brilliance and vitreous polish luster. Dispersion is strong, and pleochroism is weak.

Green is the most common color when available, but it often has a yellow component. Other color possibilities include blue, brown, purple, violet, and, on rare occasions, red. Vesuvianite may be found as well-formed crystals or aggregates, the latter massive or granular. Crystals are often prismatic or pyramidal.

Sources of facetable material include Canada, Italy, Kenya, Norway, Pakistan, Switzerland, Tanzania, and the United States; however, no consistent supply exists at present.

VESUVIANITE:	Also called *Idocrase*
Major Sources:	USA, Canada, Italy, Russia, Switzerland, Tanzania & Kenya
Colors Found:	Green, yellowish green & brownish green
Family:	Idocrase
Hardness:	6.5
Refractive Index:	1.713–1.718
Specific Gravity:	3.40
Crystal System:	Tetragonal

Pear-shaped Kenyan vesuvianite

Oval Kenyan vesuvianite

ZIRCON

ZIRCON

Zircon's **name is either derived from the Arabic word** *zarkun,* **meaning "red," or a combination of the ancient Persian words** *zar,* **meaning "gold," and** *gun,* **meaning "color." Despite this name, zircon actually occurs in a myriad of colors.**

Zircon's brilliant luster, fire, and bright hues make it an enjoyable addition to any jewelry collection.

Legends and lore

Zircon has been found in some of the most ancient archaeological sites. It has appeared in literature and the gem trade under a variety of names including *jargon* (yellow zircon), *jacinth* (red zircon), *Matura diamond* (white zircon), *starlite* (blue zircon), *hyacinth* (blue, yellow, and red zircon) and *ligure*.

Zircon is first mentioned in the ancient Indian tale of the Kalpa tree. Described by Hindu poets as the ultimate gift to the gods, it was a bright, glowing tree with bejeweled leaves of zircon.

Jewish legends say that zircon, the gemstone of fiery starlight, was the name of the guardian angel sent to watch over Adam and Eve in the Garden of Eden.

Zircon is mentioned in the Bible (using the name *jacinth* for its red variety) as being one of the "stones of fire" (Ezekiel 28:13–16) that was given to Moses and set in the breastplate of Aaron (Exodus 28:15–30). Zircon is also one of the 12 gemstones set in the foundations of the city walls of Jerusalem (Revelations 21:19) and associated with the Apostle Simon.

The Roman historian, Pliny the Elder, compared blue zircon's color to hyacinth flowers.

Traditionally, zircon is a gem of purity and innocence. It is believed to promote inner peace, while providing the wearer with wisdom, honor, and riches. Legend also has it that a zircon's loss of luster is a warning of imminent danger.

Zircon's popularity grew dramatically in the 16th century, when Italian artisans featured the gem in jewelry designs. In the 1880s, blue zircon was widely used in Victorian jewelry.

Just the facts

Although zircon's existence predates cubic zirconia by centuries, zircon is often unfairly confused with cubic zirconia. Cubic zirconia is a cheap, man-made diamond substitute that resembles colorless zircon and has a similar sounding name. While zircon may also be used as an excellent diamond substitute, it is valuable in its own right.

ZIRCON:	December's birthstone
Major Sources:	Australia, Burma, Cambodia, Nigeria, Sri Lanka, Tanzania, Thailand & Vietnam
Colors Found:	Blue, green, honey, red, white & yellow
Family:	Zircon: $ZrSiO_4$
Hardness:	6.5 to 7.5
Refractive Index:	1.81–2.02; Uniaxial (+)
Specific Gravity:	3.93–4.73
Crystal System:	Tetragonal

The fire in zircon, called *dispersion,* is caused by light entering the gemstone and separating into a prism of rainbow colors. Possessing dispersion approaching that of diamond, the brilliance of zircon is second to none. The zircon cut, a variation of the round brilliant cut that adds eight extra facets to the pavilion, was designed to take advantage of these properties.

An interesting characteristic of zircon is that its birefringence (doubly refraction, meaning that light splits into two rays as it passes through the gem) is great enough to produce visible doubling of the back facets in larger stones. Zircon also has an adamantine (diamond-like) luster, lending further credence to its suitability as a diamond substitute.

Zircon remains unscathed, while other rocks and minerals melt and reform under the tremendous heat and pressure of continental shifts, mountain building, and violent asteroid impacts. Once only considered a diamond alternative, zircon is, in fact, incredibly ancient. A tiny fragment of zircon discovered in Western Australia is the oldest known object on earth at 4.4 billion years old (the Earth formed less than 150 million years earlier). Diamonds, in comparison, are quite young—a mere one billion to 3.3 billion years old.

Cambodia is the world's premiere source for gorgeous blue zircon. Remote, pristine, and stunningly beautiful, Ratanakiri province is the major center for Cambodian zircon, yielding most of the world's finest blue zircon. Ratanakiri literally means "gemstone mountain."

Traditionally, mining took place near Bo Kheo, some 20 miles from the provincial seat of Ban Lung. Now, though, new areas have been opened. South of Ban Lung, a mining camp exists in the forest, where workers toil to extract Ratanakiri zircon from narrow mine shafts that tap into an alluvial layer about 15 feet below the surface.

From left to right: Ratanakiri zircon, champagne zircon, and fancy zircon

Tanzanian imperial zircon

ZULTANITE® DIASPORE

Astonishingly beautiful, durable, exotic, and rare, *Zultanite® diaspore* is an extraordinary gemstone. Like tanzanite, it is so rare that it is only found in one location worldwide—high in Turkey's Anatolian Mountains. It is a rising star in fine jewelry, and it's easy to fall in love with its sparklingly brilliant, tranquil, earthy colors. JTV is delighted to extend the privilege of owning this phenomenal gemstone to our valued customers.

First faceted in the late seventies (1977), Zultanite® diaspore is an extremely rare gemstone that, despite its beauty and suitability for jewelry, was previously plagued by scant availability. While an article in *Gems & Gemology* magazine (Winter 1994) indicated that supplies were promising, this hasn't translated into the availability of good-quality gems until recently. While some jewelers previously sourced limited quantities of this gem marketed under their mineral name *diaspore*, please don't confuse the two.

This mineral's name comes from the Greek word *diaspora*, meaning "to scatter." While diaspore was discovered in Mramorskoi, Kossoibrod, Ural Mountains, Russia, in 1801, the Turkish deposit remains the world's only source of this gemstone. Zultanite® diaspore was named by Murat Akgun in honor of the 36 sultans who founded the Ottoman Empire in Anatolia in the late 13th century.

Legends and lore

Some people believe this diaspore can assist in the development of psychic power, astral force, ambition, intellect, desire, and emotions based on intellect and touch.

Just the facts

The beauty and intrigue of this regal, transparent gemstone are in its different colors. Many of these gems show a slight color shift from a kiwi green to a raspberry purplish pink, depending on the light source. Incredibly, they can also exhibit

ZULTANITE:	Color shift
Major Sources:	Turkey
Colors Found:	Various (see opposite)
Family:	Diaspore: AlO(OH)
Hardness:	6.5 to 7
Refractive Index:	1.70–1.75; Biaxial (+)
Specific Gravity:	3.30–3.39
Crystal System:	Orthorhombic

khaki greens, sage greens, cognac pinks, pinkish champagnes, and gingers. The kiwi greens with canary flashes are noticeable under daylight, while incandescent lighting will elicit rich champagne, pink, or raspberry hues. Darker raspberry shades are caused by higher manganese content. According to the leading gemstone author Antoinette Matlins, some women prefer the colors of this gemstone because they like the more subtle pastel contrast and find they complement earth tones (green, brown, and gold), making the gem more wearable.

Some diaspores also possess the coveted cat's-eye effect. This chatoyancy is a reflection effect that appears as a single bright band of light across the surface of a gemstone.

Although it was initially collected by mineral enthusiasts and independent miners in the mid-eighties, diaspore is now mined commercially. Mined by hand with chisels and pick-axes in Turkey's Anatolian Mountains (Milas county of Mugla) at a height of over 4,000 feet, the world's only deposit is seven miles away from the nearest village of Selimiye. But its rarity isn't just dictated by its natural scarcity and remoteness. It tests the skills of even experienced cutters due to the difficulty in correctly orienting each crystal to accentuate its inherent beauty. With up to 98% of the crystal lost during cutting, its unbelievably low yield (2%) really reinforces the exclusivity of this truly beautiful gemstone, and it is one of the reasons it is so rare, especially in larger sizes (over five carats).

ANNIVERSARY GEMS

1st Gold Jewelry	13th Citrine	30th Pearl Jubilee
2nd Garnet	14th Opal	35th Emerald
3rd Pearl	15th Ruby	39th Cat's-Eye Chrysoberyl
4th Blue Topaz	16th Peridot	40th Ruby
5th Sapphire	17th Amethyst	45th Sapphire
6th Amethyst	18th Cat's-Eye Chrysoberyl	50th Golden Jubilee
7th Onyx	19th Garnet	52nd Star Ruby
8th Tourmaline	20th Emerald	55th Alexandrite
9th Lapis Lazuli	21st Iolite	60th Diamond Jubilee
10th Diamond Jewelry	22nd Spinel	65th Star Sapphire
11th Turquoise	23rd Imperial Topaz	70th Sapphire Jubilee
12th Jade	24th Tanzanite	75th Diamond
	25th Silver Jubilee	80th Ruby Jubilee

Although these gemstones are associated with wedding anniversaries, many people give them as gifts to celebrate all kinds of events.

INDEX